P9-API-861

RIPPLE EFFECTS

John McInnes
Mimi Garry
Emily Hearn
Margaret Hughes

NELSON CANADA

Published in 1983 by
Nelson Canada,
A Division of International Thomson Limited
1120 Birchmount Road
Scarborough, Ontario
M1K 5G4

ISBN 0-17-602002-0

Canadian Cataloguing in Publication Data

Main entry under title:
Ripple effects

(LDR networks)
For use in elementary schools.
ISBN 0-17-602002-0

1. Readers (Elementary) 2. Readers—1950-
I. McInnes, John, 1927- II. Series: Networks
(Toronto, Ont.)

PE1119.R56 1983 428.6 C83-098968-4

Printed and bound in Canada

Design: Rob McPhail
Theme Openers:
Three-Dimensional Illustrations: David Chang and Mark Craig; photographed by Michael Kohn/Oyster Studio
Cover:
Paper Sculpture: David Chang;
photographed by Michael Cohn/Oyster Studio
Diver Photograph: Paul Schutt © 1983
Typography: David Taylor/Taylor/Levkoe Associates
Typesetting: Trigraph Inc.
Film: Herzig Somerville Limited
Printing: Ashton Potter Limited
Herzig Somerville Limited (cover)

Illustrations
David Bathurst: 140-145; Ron Berg: 52-55, 164-175; Lynda Cooper/Cooperart, Inc.: 130-137; Amanda Duffy: 146-153; Mary Jane Gerber: 94-95; Elaine Macpherson/ Elaine Macpherson Enterprises, Ltd.: 76-87; Jock MacRae: 8-13, 106-118, 154-162; Paul McCusker: 23-28, 177, 189, 191; Debi Perna: 56-61; Glenn Priestley: 16-21; Barbara Reid: 15; Sharon Smith/Inkwell Artwork, Inc.: 98-105.

Photographs
American Mining Congress: 36 top; Ronald Caplan: 89, 91, 92; Rodney Catanach; 39; The Cousteau Society, Inc., 930 West 21st Street, Norfolk, VA 23517, a membership supported environmental organization: 38; Earl Gerber: 62-63; Joseph MacInnis: 45; Jack McKenney: 33 bottom, 34 bottom; Burton McNeely/ Masterfile: 33 top; Miller Services: 37, 65-69; NASA: 32; © National Geographic Society: 40, 43, 49; Birgitte Nielsen: 119-123; Public Archives Canada: 88; Paul Schutt © 1983:1, 34 top; Scripps Institute of Oceanography: 36 bottom; Leslie Shedden: 93; Woods Hole Oceanographic Institution: 35.

Stamps on pages 72-75 courtesy of Gordon Keith, Empire Stamp Company, Toronto, Ontario.

Acknowledgements
For their assistance during the preparation of *Ripple Effects*, the authors would like to express their gratitude to the following content consultants.

Undersea Exploration: Dr. Richard Winterbottom, Associate Curator of Ichthyology and Herpetology, Royal Ontario Museum

Horses in the Coal Mines: Mike Grice, Mining Engineer, Nova Scotia Department of Mines and Energy, Halifax, Nova Scotia

Permission to reprint copyrighted material is gratefully acknowledged. Information that will enable the publisher to rectify error or omission will be welcomed.

"Undersea" from *Underwater Man* by Joseph MacInnis is reprinted by permission of The Canadian Publishers, McClelland and Stewart, Toronto.

"The Fox and the Grapes" from *Aesop's Fables* retold by Anne Terry White, copyright © 1964 by Anne Terry White, is adapted and reprinted by permission of Random House, Inc.

"The Boy Who Cried Wolf" from *Aesop* by James Reeves is reprinted by the kind permission of the Blackie Publishing Group.

"Maybe, a Mole" by Julia Cunningham, copyright © 1974 by Julia Cunningham, is reprinted by permission of Pantheon Books, a division of Random House, Inc.

"Footprints" from *FEATHERED ONES AND FURRY* by Aileen Fisher (Thomas Y. Crowell), copyright © 1971 by Aileen Fisher, is reprinted by permission of Harper & Row, Publishers, Inc.

"Crossing the Creek" is excerpted from chapters 2 and 3 of *Little House on the Prairie* by Laura Ingalls Wilder, copyright 1935 as to text by Laura Ingalls Wilder; renewed 1963 by Roger L. MacBride. Reprinted by permission of Harper & Row, Publishers, Inc.

"Horses in the Coal Mines" by Ron Caplan is adapted and excerpted from an article in Cape Breton's Magazine, Number 32. Used by permission of the author, Ronald Caplan.

"The Pit Ponies" from *Merlin and the Snake's Egg* by Leslie Norris, copyright © 1978 by Leslie Norris, is reprinted by permission of Viking Penguin Inc.

"The Top" reprinted by permission of the author, Colleen Thibaudeau.

Untitled poem from page 65 of *Dogs & Dragons, Trees and Dreams: A Collection of Poems* by Karla Kuskin, copyright © 1972 by Karla Kuskin, is reprinted by permission of Harper & Row, Publishers, Inc.

"How to Brush Your Teeth" is reprinted from *Learning With Computers*, by permission of the author, Virlie Sleightholm.

All other selections are used by permission of the authors.

Contents

HORSE POWER

CALLING ALL DETECTIVES

EYE CATCHERS

GETTING TOGETHER

JOURNEY THROUGH THE STARS

Messages

by John McInnes

Messages
Enclosed in envelopes, carrying your name
Scribbled on the backs of pretty postcards
Stuck magnetically onto refrigerator doors
Addressed to you in shouts or whispers
Given warmly in a hug or handshake
Extended silently with a wink or smile
Sent to you mysteriously, in the night
  dream-wrapped.
Messages
  written and read
  spoken and heard
  unwritten, unread
  unspoken, unheard
Messages.

MESSAGE MOSAIC

The Mind Reader

by Jean Booker

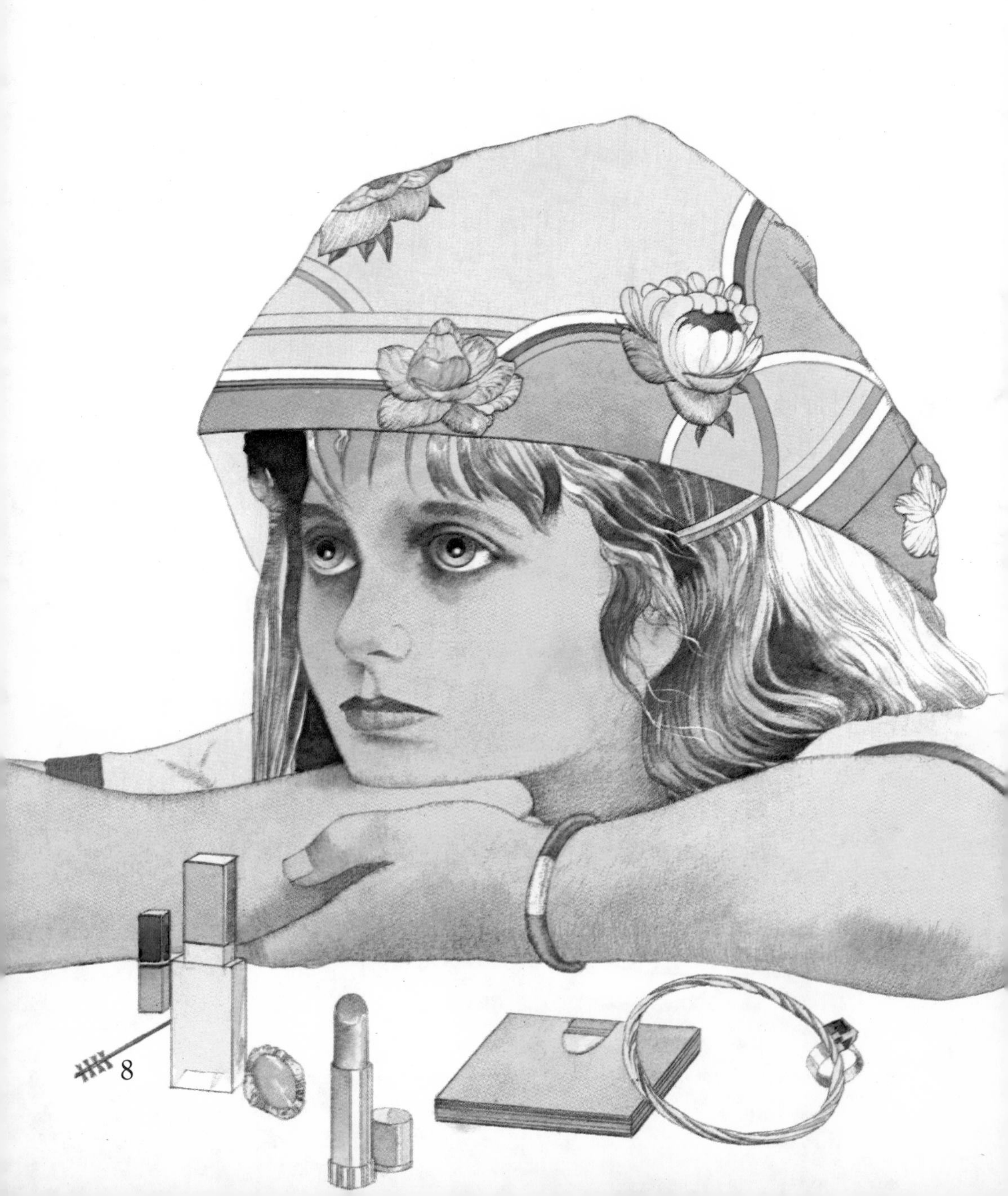

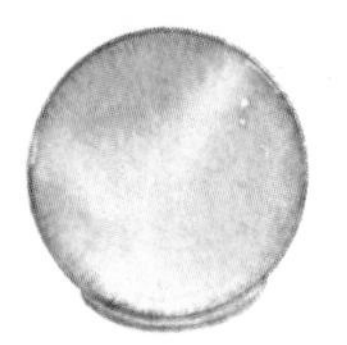

"Dorothy Rogers can tell fortunes!" "Dorothy can predict the future!" "Dorothy is a mind reader."

Dorothy knew what the other students in her class said about her. Sometimes she overheard them whispering to each other. Sometimes they joked with Dorothy about her superpowers. And sometimes they said things that hurt her feelings. Like the time Alex Porter yelled at her, "Come on, mind reader, tell us what's going to be on our exam!" It was a problem to have a reputation for being able to tell the future.

Dorothy usually joked about her mysterious powers. She didn't think she was special in any way. She watched things happen around her, and she listened carefully. Often she seemed to have good ideas about what was going to happen next.

Usually when Dorothy told someone what was going to happen, she was just trying to be helpful. When Carlos Lopez lost his Siamese cat, Dorothy suggested that he would find her if he looked for a box with some of his old clothes in it. She suggested that he should look in a high place. Carlos found the cat with three new kittens in a box in the garage, where he hadn't thought of looking. Of course, he told the class about Dorothy's "supermind."

Then there was the time Dorothy told Yvette's little sister that she might get a bike for her birthday if she was good. She did it to stop the little girl from crying when she fell and hurt herself. The next day Dorothy was glad to hear that her prediction had come true. Yvette's sister told everybody that Dorothy knew magic.

When it was time for the school Fall Fair to raise money for charity, Dorothy's friends got a great idea. At least it seemed like a great idea to them. They would set up a fortune-telling tent so that Dorothy could tell fortunes. Before Dorothy could stop them, they had set up a committee to plan the event.

"Oh, come on, Dorothy," said her best friend, Farida. "It will be fun. You can dress up in a head scarf and hoop earrings, and tell people what's going to happen to them. It doesn't matter if it's true or not. People will know it's just for fun."

"I have an old fish bowl you can use as your crystal ball," said Yvette. "We can make a lot of money. We'll call you 'Zee Great Madame Dorothy.'"

Dorothy laughed along with the girls. However, she was a little afraid of the idea.

Alex Porter wasn't on the committee, but of course he had to put in his two cents worth. "I wouldn't let any creepy fortune-teller look into *my* head," he said. "Our Fall Fair would be a better place without her."

Dorothy ignored Alex. She didn't know why he was so rude to her. She also had a funny feeling he wouldn't be at the Fall Fair.

"All three of us can be fortune-tellers," suggested Dorothy to her friends Yvette and Farida. "You can tell fortunes as well as I can. Just say the first thing that comes into your head."

For the next two weeks the whole class worked hard getting ready for the fair. They made posters. They collected old toys and books to sell. They set up a bean-bag toss and a fish-pond game. Yvette counted out dried beans to put into a big jar. She made a sign saying "Win a prize. Guess the number of beans in the jar." The class got permission to set up some video games in a tent. They blew up balloons and got funny costumes together.

When the day of the Fall Fair came, Dorothy felt a little nervous about the fortune-telling act. On the other hand, she knew that if she was wrong a lot, she could get rid of her reputation, and the kids would start treating her as an ordinary person. Dorothy had a feeling it wasn't going to be easy—even if there were three fortune-tellers, not just one.

To Dorothy's disappointment, Yvette and Farida backed out at the last minute. They said the tent was going to be so busy that both of them would have to sell tickets and keep people in line. Besides, they said, it would look more like serious business if Dorothy were sitting in the tent alone in all that fortune-teller's gear.

Dorothy's friend Terry was the first to come into the tent. He thought it was great fun. "Hi, Madame Dorothy," he said. "Tell me if I'll be lucky today."

"You will be," said Dorothy in a strange voice.

"I'm going to guess there are nine hundred and thirty-eight beans in that jar out there."

"Your lucky number," laughed Dorothy.

"And I'll win a baseball glove," said Terry.

Dorothy looked into her crystal ball. "Whammo!" she declared.

Dorothy's next customer was her teacher.

"I see you are going on a long journey," said Dorothy. "There are palm trees waving on a beach."

"You're right," said her teacher. "I'm going to Jamaica during March break. What a smart fortune-teller you are!"

There were lots of customers crowding into the tent. With each one, Dorothy said the first thing that came into her head. Sometimes she said crazy things just so she would be sure to be wrong.

About three o'clock in the afternoon Farida came in to tell Dorothy that the Fall Fair was getting ready to close. She said to Dorothy, "How about one more hot prediction. How much money did our fortune-telling tent make today?"

"At twenty-five cents a fortune, I'd say we made twenty-nine dollars and seventy-five cents!"

"Almost right on the nose!" said Farida. "You're fantastic, Dorothy. We had one hundred and twenty customers, counting me."

"And *you* didn't pay," laughed Dorothy.

She and Farida and Yvette went back to Dorothy's house with their costumes and props.

On the way Yvette asked Dorothy the question everyone wanted answered. "Dorothy, how do you do it? Do you really have special powers?"

"My grandmother was a fortune-teller," said Dorothy, "and she — "

"Come on, Dorothy, tell us the truth," said Farida. "Terry won the guessing contest, and he said you predicted he would."

"That was easy," said Dorothy. "I overheard Yvette counting the beans. When Terry told me his guess, I knew he'd win. Do you always count out loud, Yvette?"

"I'm so terrible at math, I whisper so that I won't lose track," admitted Yvette.

"I get it," said Farida. "And you heard Yvette counting quarters, too, outside the tent. That's how you knew how much money we made."

"Of course," said Dorothy. "And I knew you were sneaking a free fortune."

"But what about our teacher's trip?" asked Yvette. "She said you told her future exactly."

"Nothing to it. I saw her at the travel agency the other day. With all those folders about Jamaica, I figured that's where she was going."

"And my sister's birthday bike?" asked Yvette.

"Oh, that! It was a piece of cake. I happened to see a delivery person take a box into your house. It was just the right shape for a bike," said Dorothy.

"But what about Carlos's cat?" asked Farida. "I suppose you had a dream about a garage."

"Lucky again," replied Dorothy. "I happen to know a lot about Siamese cats. They like high places. Cats who are about to have kittens like a safe place, but they also like familiar smells. I just put two and two together. I figured that Carlos's cat would like a box with some of his old clothes in it."

"You're a fake after all!" laughed Yvette. "Can we tell the other kids your secrets?"

"I hope you will," said Dorothy. "I think they'll believe you."

"I can't wait to tell Alex Porter," said Farida. "I'll tell him that you're not a mind reader. You're just someone who uses her eyes and ears better than most other people."

"I didn't see Alex at the fair today. I wonder if he's sick or something," said Yvette.

Dorothy had a feeling that Alex might not be at school for a few days. She quickly decided to keep that information to herself.

"I wonder what we'll do at next year's Fall Fair," said Farida.

"Not fortune-telling," said Dorothy. "With the new reputation I'm going to have, we wouldn't make a quarter. I'm sure the three of us will still be friends next year at this time. We'll probably imitate a famous trio of female singers. Of course, that's only a guess."□

Unsaid (for reading out loud)

by Andrew Donaldson

Sometimes it's good to say things FAST
The first word comes tumbling-out-just-before-the-last,
Like, "Don't step on that-banana-peel!"
Or, "Get out of the WAY, I'M HOLDING AN EEL!"

Some things are better when you say them . . . s . . . l . . . o . . . w . . . l . . . y
Letting each word loll lllazzzily on your tongue
Before letting it go,
Like, "Hot dogs . . . relish . . . ice . . . creeeeamm!"
Or, "I've just dreamed the most . . . delicious . . . dreammmmm!"

Some things are best when you say them softly
"I love you,"
Or, "Hush, be still, the baby's sleeping."

SOME THINGS ARE GREAT WHEN YOU YELL THEM OUT LOUDLY
YOU FILL UP YOUR LUNGS
AND YOU KNOCK 'EM DOWN DEAD!

And some things are better left
Unsaid.

The Door

by Dorothy-Jane Goulding

This story is about a mysterious event that happened to me. You may not believe me—many people don't—but I swear that every word of it is true.

It all started when Mom and Dad bought our house. The house was falling to pieces, but my parents like to fix things up, and the house was cheap. They said they could do most of the repairs themselves, and that when they were finished, the house would be really handsome. They were right, too. The work took them almost three years, but the house looks great now, and we're all happy living in it.

The house is over a hundred years old. It used to have a back part, but that burned down or something. Anyway, only the front part was still standing when we moved in. There were three bedrooms upstairs—one for me, one for my younger brother Brian, and one for Mom and Dad. The place was a mess. There were chunks of plaster everywhere, and the floors sagged. All the windows rattled in the wind, and the doors didn't fit. Mom and Dad wanted the house to be weather-tight before winter, so they got to work right away. They even let me help a bit with the simple jobs.

The dream started a few nights after we moved in. It was a funny kind of dream, not a nightmare exactly, but so real that it stayed in my mind all the next day. There was a door, and someone behind the door was trying to open it. I wanted to help, but I was scared because I didn't know who was behind the door. Before I could make up my mind whether to help or not, I woke up.

That's all there was to it, and thinking about it afterwards, it was no big thing. Except that, the next night I had the dream again. It was the same door, and I still had the feeling that I ought to help, but I was still too scared. When I woke up, I was really puzzled. People don't dream the same dreams very often, and I wondered if the dream would come again.

It did, a few nights later. This time, when I tried to walk away from the door, my feet stuck. I woke up suddenly, in a cold sweat. That morning after breakfast, when Brian and I were walking to school, I told him about the door.

"What do you think?" I asked.

Brian was silent for a minute, and then he said, "Why don't you just forget about it, Judy? Maybe you keep dreaming about the same thing because you think about it so much during the day."

Brian looked as if he were going to say more, but he stopped. We were both silent till we got to school.

After that Brian and I didn't talk about the door again. Sometimes I dreamed the dream, and sometimes I didn't. I got sort of used to it, but I still wondered why it kept happening.

Then one night I heard Mom and Dad talking in the kitchen. They were both tired. It was hard work trying to keep the household going around the mess they had made, tearing down walls and ripping up floors. I heard Dad say, "Look, this is all very inconvenient for us both, but it won't last forever. Let's take tomorrow evening off, just the two of us, and go out for dinner and an early movie. OK?"

Mom must have agreed, because later on she came into the living room and told Brian and me that she and Dad were going out the next night without us.

"We won't be late," she promised. "I know you haven't been alone in the house before, but you'll be all right, won't you? I could try to get a sitter, if you'd feel more comfortable."

Neither Brian nor I wanted a sitter. We told Mom

we'd be fine by ourselves. So then she said she'd leave supper in the oven, and she told us about dishes and things like that. We promised to take care of everything.

The next evening when Mom and Dad were ready to leave, Dad said to me, "By the way, Judy, I got started in that back room today, and I've pulled down a lot of plaster. You two had better stay out of there or you'll track plaster dust all over the rest of the house."

When Mom and Dad opened the front door to leave, we saw that a thunderstorm had begun. The wind was howling and the rain was coming down in sheets. For a moment I thought Mom and Dad would change their minds and stay home, but Mom just laughed and said they'd have to run to the car. In a minute they were gone.

Brian and I had our supper and did the dishes together. I had planned to watch TV for a while before doing my homework, but the reception was bad, so I played a game with Brian instead. Then I decided to go and look at what Dad had done to the back room. I knew that if I stayed in the hall and just peeked in, I wouldn't track any mess around.

Dad had laid an old sheet across the bottom edge of the door because of the dust, but I pulled it away and carefully turned the knob. I opened the door to let the light from the hall shine in, and then I saw something that made my heart thump.

The outside back wall had been covered with plaster, and where Dad had pulled the plaster away, there was a door. It didn't lead anywhere now, of course, because that was where the old part of the house had begun, and the old part wasn't there any more. But the scary thing was—it was *my* door, the door in my dream.

The wind howled and the door began to rattle.

I stared at it, just as I had in my dream. More than anything, I wanted to open that door.

Suddenly Brian was beside me, grabbing my arm. "It's the door, isn't it?" he asked.

I looked at him in astonishment.

"How do you know?" I asked.

"Because I've dreamed the dream too. Not every night, but off and on."

Brian had dreamed about the door too? I could scarcely believe it. But if he had, I thought quickly, then the dream really must mean something.

"Shall I open it?" I asked.

He nodded. "You have to," he said. "But Judy, I'm scared."

"So am I," I admitted. "But I've made up my mind. I'm going to settle this thing right now. You can go back to the living room and wait for me if you want to."

Brian shook his head and said he'd stay.

Dad's tool box lay on the floor near my feet. I picked up the hammer and the screwdriver. I walked across the room towards the door. As I was looking for a good place to start prying, I suddenly felt a pull. We both felt it. Neither one of us could have turned away from that door even if we had wanted to.

"What'll we do if you can't open it?" asked Brian. "It must have been shut for years and years."

I didn't answer. I'd just found a crack between the frame and the door, so I forced the screwdriver in and pried hard. Even above the noise of the storm, Brian and I both heard a creak. And as we watched, the nails began to give.

"Keep at it, Judy," said Brian, biting his lip.

I kept on prying with the screwdriver, driving it in farther with the hammer, and prying again. Bit by bit the door began to come away from the frame. The wind whistled through the crack, and all of a sudden the door seemed to burst open on its own. Brian and I were flung back across the room, and the rain and dead leaves from the yard came swirling in after us.

Then the inside door to the hall slammed shut, and we were left in darkness. Brian yelled, and I guess I let out a yelp too. Clutching each other, we looked fearfully towards the open doorway.

There was no one there. Yet we both had the most wonderful feeling of peace. It was as though something, or someone, was terribly grateful, and letting us know. We gazed at each other in the light from the street beyond the garden, and I could tell from Brian's face that he felt the same as I did. We started to laugh, and then we noticed that the wind had dropped. The door was just swinging quietly to and fro.

I got the hammer and nailed the door shut again. Then we both wiped our feet carefully and left the room, closing the door behind us. I even remembered to replace Dad's sheet across the bottom edge.

We decided not to say anything to Mom and Dad. There was nothing to tell, really. Besides, how could we explain that feeling we'd both had, and who would ever believe we'd both been dreaming the same dream?

A week or so later, on the way to school, Brian said, "That was a lot of junk, wasn't it, about that door?"

"What do you mean?" I asked. "You were there. You know what happened as well as I do."

"Oh, Judy," he said, "you don't think I was telling the truth about your stupid dream, do you? I just played along, to see what you'd do."

"But—" I started to argue with Brian, and then I stopped. I could tell he'd never admit how scared he'd been, or that we had really dreamed the same dream.

I've never dreamed about that door again. And whatever Brian says, I know he wasn't fooling that night. For some reason, he doesn't want to remember what happened. But I know that someone was behind that door. I know that we let him—or her—out. And I'm not afraid to say so.□

Black Shadow

by Raymond Bradbury

As the camper lurched off the highway onto a gravel lane, Dave almost fell off his bunk. He lost his place in the comic book he was reading. Quickly flipping through the book, he found the page again.

> ***At the entrance to the mine, Black Shadow—an evil leer on his cruel face—slowly opened the valve that would send a flood of water down upon his helpless victims.***

With a squeal of brakes, the camper stopped at the edge of a picnic area and Dave heard his mom call, "Here we are. Hopewell Rocks, New Brunswick. Put that dreadful comic book down and come out and get some fresh air."

"Just a minute, Mom," Dave called back. "I've nearly finished it."

Black Shadow, his face twisted with hatred, stared straight out of the illustrated page at Dave.

> ***"This is the end of the road for you," he was snarling at his captives. "Soon you'll be drowned like trapped rats."***

The camper door swung open.

"Out you get, Dave," his mom ordered. "You've had enough horror stories for one day. You can finish that comic book when you get back from the beach."

"But— " Dave began.

His dad's voice reached him. "Out of there, Dave! I'm going to fix dinner while your mom picks berries. Why don't you go down and take a look at the flowerpot rocks? They're supposed to be quite something."

Flinging his comic book into the corner of his camper bunk, Dave set off for the beach.

All the way down the hundreds of steps to the beach,

Black Shadow stayed in Dave's mind. He hardly noticed the other tourists who passed him on the staircase. But he did hear water lapping somewhere below.

When he reached the sand, Dave looked up and saw tall dark shapes looming all around him. Towers of red rock rose from the sand to the sky. Some were bent over and touched the cliffs, forming archways. Others stood free, their lower edges almost eaten away by the sea. High on top of the rocks small, scrubby trees clung to each other, their roots trailing down over the rock face.

The rocks do look a bit like flowerpots, Dave thought—enormous flowerpots. But instead of flowers, there were just those poor, struggling trees.

Dave wandered through a tunnel, drawn by the shining sand beyond. A boy and a girl ran past him, laughing. He found a flat rock and lay down in the sun. He wished he'd been allowed to bring *The Menace of the Black Shadow* with him so that he could finish it there on the beach.

Stretched out on the warm rock, Dave closed his eyes and listened to the sounds of the seashore. He heard the lapping of the tide and the scrunch of feet as people passed him. The last thing he heard before he dozed off was the squeaking of small birds at the edge of the water.

When a fly buzzed across Dave's face, he opened his eyes again. Still half-asleep, he gazed up at the tall rocks and the endless stairway that marked his route back to the picnic area.

Way up at the top of the stairs on the highest landing, a solitary black figure stood, dark against the sky, gazing straight down at him.

Dave leaped to his feet. "Black Shadow!" he gasped.

A young woman lowered her camera and stared at Dave in surprise.

"He—he's coming to get me," Dave stammered, staring past the woman to the cliff.

He watched fearfully as the man in black made his way slowly down the stairs. He was still far enough away that Dave could not see his face clearly.

Dave jumped off his rock and hurried to the water's edge. There the rocks would hide him from the staircase and the descending figure.

The tide was rising fast. Only a narrow strip of muddy sand remained between the rocks and the approaching waves. Small birds scooted along the tide line, dipping their long beaks into the seaweed.

Dave crouched on a small rock opposite a narrow archway. He would give Black Shadow enough time to reach the beach and walk away along the sand. Then he would dash through the stone archway and back up the staircase. But he could not afford to wait long. His strip of sand was already disappearing as the tide swiftly advanced.

Dave was sure that Black Shadow had been watching him. He even thought he remembered seeing a pair of binoculars flash in the sunlight as the man turned on the staircase.

It was colder in front of the rock face. A sharp breeze cut through Dave's shirt and made him shiver.

The tide was swirling in now, but there was still room to slip through the opening in the rock. Dave decided to count to a hundred and then make a run for it.

He had counted to eighty-seven when the archway darkened and the terrifying figure of Black Shadow appeared in the opening. Dave's escape route was blocked!

"I thought I might find you here," said Black Shadow.

Dave glanced quickly to right and left. Huge waves were rolling up to the cliffs on either side, splashing rafts of seaweed against the rocks. The only shallow space lay in front of the archway, and the water was rising above Dave's ankles.

"This is the only way out," said Black Shadow. "There's no other way."

Dave began to shake as the cold wind blew at his back. He decided that if he crouched low and ran fast through the archway, he might be able to push past Black Shadow and get away.

"Come, give me your hand and I'll help you out of here," said the black-clad figure.

What kind of trick was Black Shadow trying to pull on him, Dave wondered. Then he noticed that the man had no shoes on. His black trousers were rolled up, as if for wading. His binoculars were hanging around his neck, and between their leather straps the man wore a white collar. The face under the black hat was smiling as his big hand reached out towards Dave.

Another gust of wind came whistling through the archway, almost pushing Dave towards the man.

Dave stared at the straight, white collar. The man wore no tie.

"Are you a priest?" Dave blurted out.

"Well, not really," the man said. "I'm a minister and I'm also a bird-watcher. I was visiting a church member and stopped to do some bird watching on my way home."

Dave let himself relax. Then he remembered that he was standing almost knee-deep in chilly water. Ignoring the outstretched hand, he waded slowly towards the man.

As they climbed back up the staircase, the minister said, "I guess you're interested in sandpipers, too."

"Well, I was just . . ." Dave began.

"We get hundreds of them here this time of year," the

minister went on. "They forage on the tide line for insects."

Dave spotted his mom coming down the steps to look for him.

"Good thing I saw you walking off around the cliffs," the minister said. "I'm getting used to rescuing stranded tourists. The tide comes in fast here in the Bay of Fundy. Take care now."

Waving goodbye, the man turned and walked away. Dave waved back and then followed his mother towards the delicious smell of hamburgers.

After dinner Dave picked up *The Menace of the Black Shadow* again. He was anxious to find out how the story ended.

Leering up from the last illustration was Black Shadow. His big gnarled hands were still turning the water valve that would drown the victims in the mine. Dave turned the page. "Oh, no," he groaned. He could hardly believe his bad luck. The last page was missing from the book. It was an old copy that he had bought at a flea market, and only a torn edge showed where the page had been.

Now he would never know what fate lay in store for Black Shadow and his victims. Dave stared glumly out the camper window at the sea.

"What's wrong?" asked his mom absentmindedly. She was fiddling with the tricky catch on the camper's refrigerator door. "Wasn't it a good story?"

"It was OK," Dave answered with a shrug. Then he smiled. "The villain turned into a minister. He studied sandpipers instead of drowning people."

"That's a strange kind of ending," remarked his mother, finally pulling the fridge door open. "Would you like some butterscotch ripple ice cream for dessert?"□

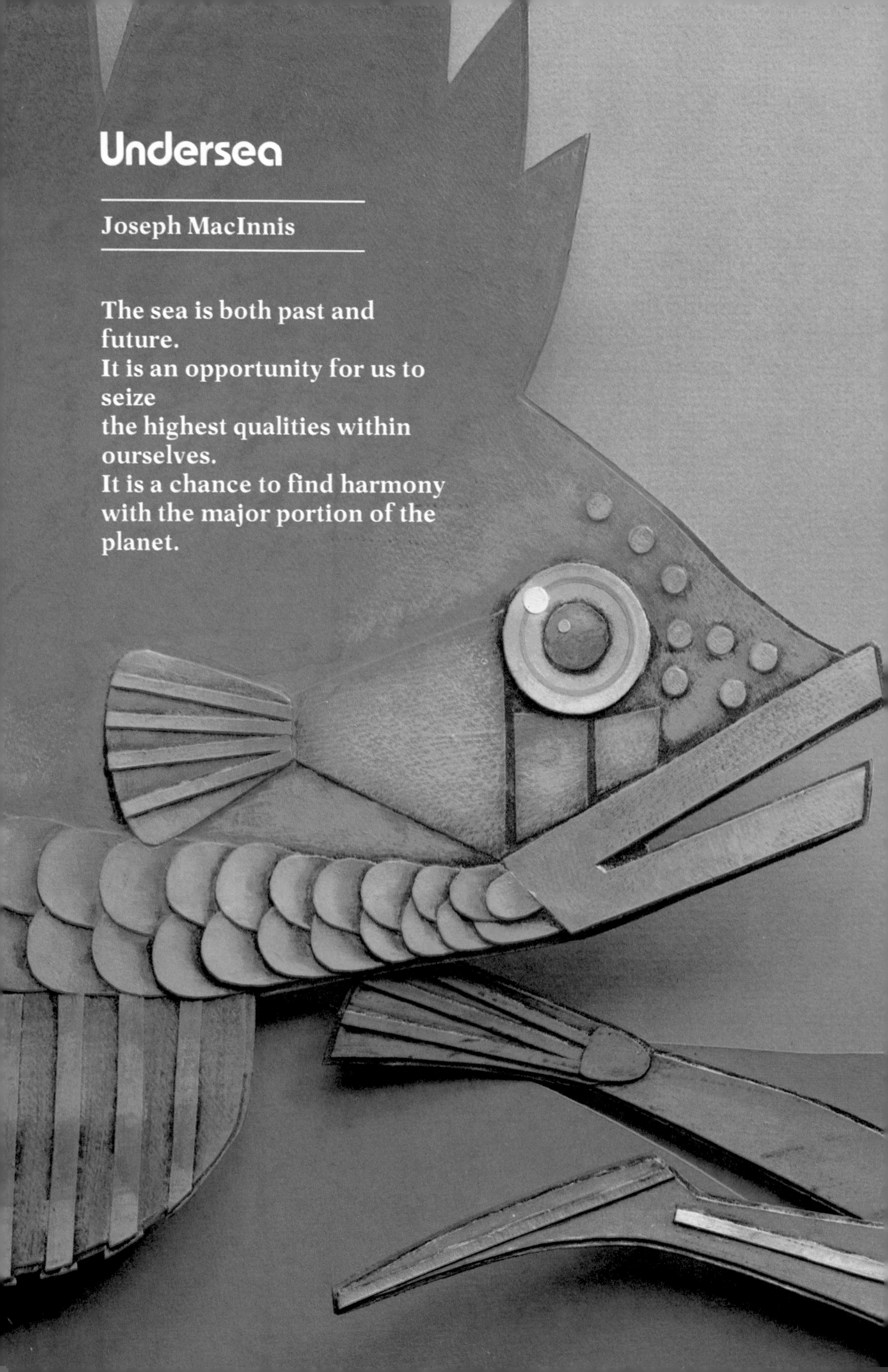

Undersea

Joseph MacInnis

The sea is both past and
future.
It is an opportunity for us to
seize
the highest qualities within
ourselves.
It is a chance to find harmony
with the major portion of the
planet.

UNDERSEA EXPLORATION UNLIMITED

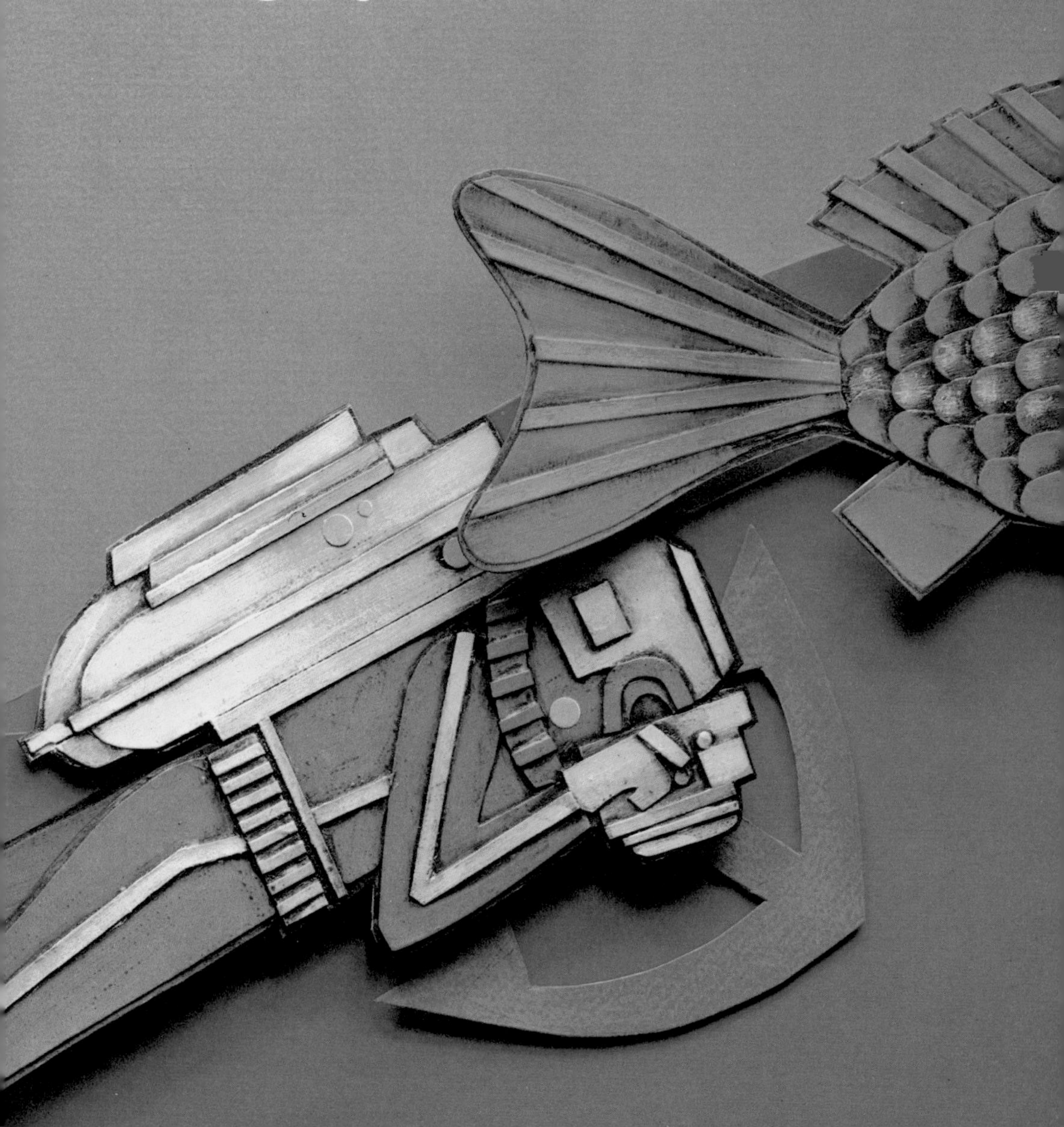

What's Going On Down There?

by Kaila Kukla

We live on a planet that has oceans. Two thirds of the earth is covered by water. What do we know about our oceans? What mysteries still lie in the canyons and valleys of the sea?

We know from fossils over two billion years old that life on earth began in the sea. What creatures live there today?

Modern equipment allows us to breathe underwater and dive with the freedom of whales. We can now search the whole ocean. We can explore it from its surface to its depths, and discover its secrets.

Let's go exploring undersea. We'll go deeper and deeper into the ocean. We'll meet ocean creatures in their underwater homes. What will they tell us about life on earth?

An underwater view. We can explore the underwater world by swimming with a snorkel and a face mask. The snorkel tube lets us breathe without lifting our heads out of water. The face mask protects our eyes and improves our underwater vision. We can study and enjoy the fascinating creatures that make their homes just beneath the surface of the ocean.

A friendly creature. While we are snorkelling, we may meet the giant whale shark—the largest fish in the ocean. When fully grown, it is as long as a trailer truck. The whale shark is a friendly creature. It is easy to approach. Some snorkellers have even taken short rides on the backs of whale sharks.

We go deeper. With proper equipment we can descend deeper into the water and enjoy the adventure of undersea exploration. A scuba tank filled with compressed air allows us to breathe underwater. A diving suit keeps us warm and helps to protect us from injury. With this equipment we can dive down into the sea to observe marine plant life and visit marine animals in their homes.

Flashlight fish? Divers who explore at night are sometimes surrounded by the glowing blue-green light of tiny fish. These fish go down into deep water during the day and come up near the surface after dark. Nutrients and oxygen in their bodies produce a cold light that helps them see to find food. In 1964 divers discovered one of these luminescent fish among the coral reefs of the Red Sea. The "flashlight fish" produces the brightest light of any creature on land or undersea. You can read your watch by the light of a single fish. This glowing creature helps to show us how living things fit into their environments in special ways.

Even deeper.... A little white-hulled submarine named *Alvin* has made scientific history. *Alvin* is only about the size of a small van. However, this sub is loaded with the latest electronic equipment and remote-control devices. On board, a team of two or three scientists is able to explore the deepest parts of the ocean and document some of the best-kept secrets of the underwater world. *Alvin* is like a spaceship of the sea.

Unknown creatures. The scientists on board *Alvin* made some surprising discoveries when they plunged 2.5 km beneath the surface of the Pacific Ocean. They found underwater hot springs called *hydrothermal vents*. The scientists also found a community of unknown creatures living around the warm-water vents. These creatures are the tube worms pictured below. The worms are blood-red. They are 7 m long, and stick out from white tubes that look like plastic. Tube worms live in total darkness at the bottom of the sea. Scientists study newly discovered creatures like the tube worms to learn how life evolves in a world without sunlight.

Minerals from the ocean floor. The ocean floor is covered with curious lumps of minerals about the size of potatoes. These lumps, or *nodules*, contain large amounts of manganese and smaller amounts of iron, copper, and nickel. The nodules form around all kinds of objects. We do not understand how and why. Sometimes a nodule will form around a shark's tooth lying on the ocean floor. People are now mining nodules in small quantities. The machinery needed to scoop them up is still very complicated and expensive. But nodules may be a valuable new source of minerals for the future.

Energy from the sun. Heat from the sun provides our world with a continuous supply of energy. Much of this solar energy falls on water, which covers two thirds of the earth's surface. The solar energy collected by the sea is equal to the energy put out by millions of nuclear power plants. Scientists are looking for ways to get this solar energy back from the sea so that we can use it.

An undersea community. Undersea homes will allow *oceanauts* to live and work in the sea for months at a time. In 1963 the undersea explorer Jacques Cousteau established the first underwater community. The Starfish House, located 10 m down in the Red Sea, was its main settlement. This underwater home kept five persons healthy and working for a month.

Home sweet home. The undersea laboratory Hydrolab is presently located about 15 m down in the Caribbean Sea near the island of St. Croix. Groups of two or three scientists live there for a week at a time. The scientists explore the area around Hydrolab for six hours a day and return to their undersea home to rest and write up notes on their research. We have come a long way in exploring the depths of the sea. But many new discoveries are waiting to be made by the next generation of oceanauts.

Beneath the Arctic Ice

Interview with Dr. Joseph MacInnis

by Virginia Gosling Mainprize

Dr. Joseph MacInnis is a world-famous Arctic diver. He is also a writer, explorer, photographer, film maker, and medical doctor. He is the first person to dive and take photographs under the ice at the North Pole. Dr. MacInnis has looked after divers on some of the world's longest and deepest dives. He is the man who took Prince Charles diving under the Arctic ice. And he is the man who found the lost *Breadalbane*, a sailing ship that sank in the Arctic in 1853.

INTERVIEWER: How did you decide to become a diver?

DR. MacINNIS: I loved to swim when I was a boy, and I have always been fascinated by the sea. When I grew up, I went to medical school and studied to be a doctor. Then I decided to combine two of my main interests by becoming a diving doctor.

INTERVIEWER: What do you do?

DR. MacINNIS: I study what people's bodies can and cannot do underwater. I also test new equipment that helps people breathe, stay underwater longer, and move through the water more easily. I am interested in finding out how humans adapt to new and sometimes very harsh environments. Because of my research, we are exploring places that were impossible to reach before. We can now dive deeper than ever before, and into much colder water.

INTERVIEWER: You're doing most of your present work in the Arctic. Isn't that one of the harshest environments a human being can explore?

DR. MacINNIS: Yes. It is the most hostile and dangerous environment on earth. The conditions are so harsh that one mistake can mean death.

Dr. Joseph MacInnis with Remote Piloted Vehicle. The vehicle is equipped with powerful lights and television and still cameras

INTERVIEWER: One of the harsh conditions must be the extreme cold. How cold does it get in the Arctic?

DR. MacINNIS: Sometimes the temperature on land is –45°C with fierce winds. The water temperature is usually about –2°C. In order to get into the water, we often have to chop a hole through ice that is more than 1.5 m thick.

INTERVIEWER: People would die very quickly in water that cold if they weren't protected. How do you keep warm?

DR. MacINNIS: We wear special suits made of tiny cells of *neoprene*, a kind of rubber. And we pump warm air into our suits to protect us from the icy water outside. But if we tore the rubber or punctured it, our suits would fill with water. And the weight of our heavy lead belts would sink us. We must also be careful not to let any water slip past the mouthpieces of our air tanks into our mouths. Even a tiny sip of freezing water would cause our throats to squeeze shut and prevent us from breathing. So you see, we have to be very careful all the time.

INTERVIEWER: Have you developed other equipment that helps you to explore these icy waters?

DR. MacINNIS: Yes. We have developed the *Sub-Igloo*. It is the first under-ice dive station in the northern polar sea. It is just what its name suggests—a sort of igloo under the ice. The Sub-Igloo is a giant transparent bubble that floats deep underwater, and is held in place by eight tonnes of ballast. It's warm and dry inside, and there is fresh air. A Sub-Igloo is like an explorer's tent. It's a place where divers can go if they're tired or in trouble. It's a place to store equipment. It's also a place for divers to communicate. We can take off our face masks and talk to each other, or talk by telephone with people above the ice.

A Sub-Igloo in Arctic waters

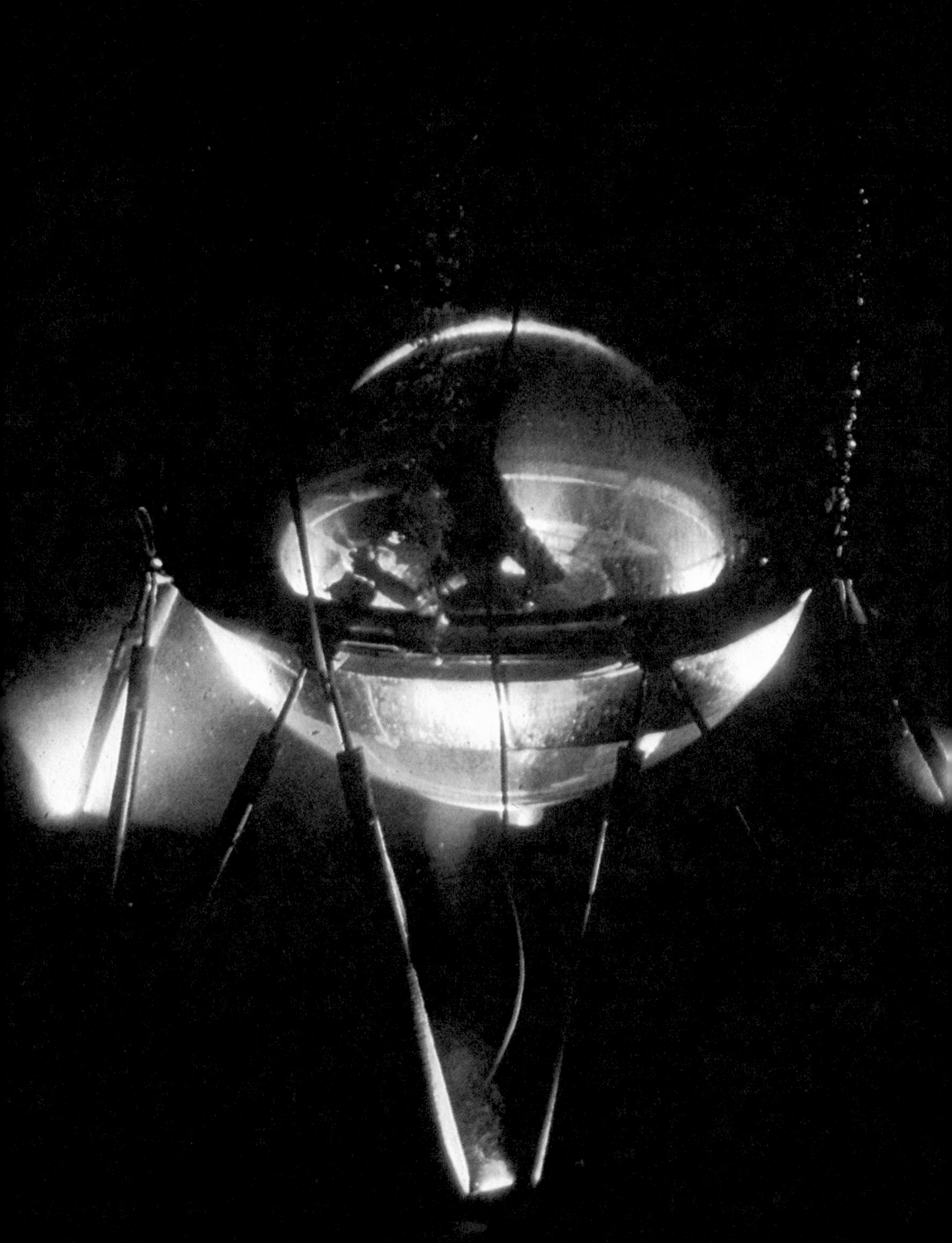

INTERVIEWER: Do any plants or animals live in the Arctic waters?

DR. MacINNIS: When I first went to the Arctic, I expected to find an underwater desert. Like most people, I didn't think that many plants or animals could live in such cold water. But I've been amazed to discover how much undersea life there actually is. The seafloor is covered with plants and animals. Between the rocks there are anemones—small flower-like creatures with tentacles waving in the current. There are also other creatures like mussels, snails, jellyfish, sea urchins, clams, and starfish. And, of course, there are seals and polar bears.

INTERVIEWER: Have you ever come close to a polar bear?

DR. MacINNIS: Oh, yes, and they are huge and frightening animals. Once we were in our inflatable boat when suddenly, 30 m away, the huge white head of a polar bear surged forward out of the water. The bear swung towards us, glaring. It moved smoothly through the water with its enormous, shovel-sized paws. The razor-sharp claws on those paws could have shredded our boat in seconds. I was terrified. Here was the king of the Arctic, one of the few creatures on earth that hunts human beings for food. We slowed down our motor, and the bear swam away from us towards the shore. We didn't see it again.

INTERVIEWER: Was that your most dangerous experience?

DR. MacINNIS: No. My most dangerous experience happened when I least expected it. We had been diving under the ice, and had finished our work for the day. Another diver and I went down for one last check.

Diver with powerful light beneath the Arctic ice at the North Pole

The water was clear and calm. There was no current. When I started back up to look for the dive hole, I couldn't find it! The hole had vanished in the glare of sunlight that filtered through the ice. We were lost. We couldn't tell where we had come from, and we didn't know where to go. We tried to stay calm and keep our breathing steady to save air. Then, suddenly, the dive hole appeared above us just as suddenly as it had disappeared.

INTERVIEWER: What was your most exciting experience?

DR. MacINNIS: My most thrilling experience was coming face to face with a bowhead whale. The bowhead lives in a remote part of the Arctic. It has been hunted nearly to extinction and is very rare. I was filming beluga whales in Alaska in March 1973. While I was swimming, I suddenly came face to face with a 15 m bowhead. I was frightened at first, but there was no need to be. The bowhead rose to the surface and stayed there for a few seconds. It sucked in a roomful of air and slowly went down again like a mountain sinking into the sea. Then, slowly, it swam away from me.

INTERVIEWER: Have you seen many other whales in the Arctic?

DR. MacINNIS: Perhaps the most interesting whale I've seen up close is the narwhal. Narwhals are 4 m to 6 m long, and the male has a 3 m tusk growing out of his upper jaw. I once swam right into the middle of a group of them.

INTERVIEWER: What did the whales do?

DR. MacINNIS: Narwhals are peace-loving mammals and won't attack. They were curious, though. They rolled over on their backs to get a better look at me.

INTERVIEWER: Dr. MacInnis, one of your most exciting discoveries was the lost ship *Breadalbane*. Could you tell us some of her history?

DR. MacINNIS: The *Breadalbane* had been lost under polar ice for a hundred and thirty years. She set out from England in 1853 to look for Captain John Franklin and his crew, who had disappeared in the Arctic while searching for the Northwest Passage. But in August of that year, the *Breadalbane*'s hull was crushed by the ice somewhere off the coast of Beechey Island. All her crew escaped and the ship sank within fifteen minutes.

INTERVIEWER: How did you first hear of the *Breadalbane*?

DR. MacINNIS: I first heard of her in 1975. It was just a rumour, but some people believed that a sunken ship lay somewhere off Beechey Island. Once I heard the story, I knew I had to try to find her.

INTERVIEWER: Wasn't it like looking for a needle in a haystack?

DR. MacINNIS: Yes. Some people thought I was crazy to look for a ship less than 40 m long, buried somewhere under thousands of square kilometres of ice. They thought I was crazy to try to find her in waters that are ice-free for only a few weeks of the year, where winds are dangerous and unpredictable, and where icebergs weigh more than a million tonnes. But even as a boy I had always dreamed of finding a shipwreck, and I knew this was the one I had to find.

INTERVIEWER: What, exactly, did you think you'd find?

DR. MacINNIS: I knew that if the *Breadalbane* had not been smashed by the icebergs that scraped along the bottom of the sea where she lay, we would find her perfectly preserved. Most wooden ships that go down in shallow water are destroyed quickly.

They're either smashed by waves or eaten by worms. But under the ice in the clear, cold waters of the Arctic, the *Breadalbane* would have been protected. The ship would be a perfect time capsule. She would look exactly as she had a hundred and thirty years ago. Even the personal belongings of the sailors would be preserved.

INTERVIEWER: How did you find her?

DR. MacINNIS: It took a lot of hard work. But we had a fantastic crew and some incredible equipment. After two unsuccessful expeditions, we finally located the *Breadalbane* in 1980. We found her by using a *side-scan sonar*, a machine that records what the ocean floor looks like. We found her completely intact. Even her masts were standing. The next year we went back and took photographs with a remote-control camera. And on my most recent and most exciting expedition, we actually went down and touched the *Breadalbane*, perfectly preserved for a hundred and thirty years beneath the Arctic ice.

INTERVIEWER: That must have been a thrilling experience. But are you ever scared when you dive?

DR. MacINNIS: Yes, sometimes. But most of the time I love diving. There are some perfect times when everything feels right, when I feel in complete harmony with the world. And there are times I have lots of fun, too.

INTERVIEWER: How do you have fun when you are working so hard?

DR. MacINNIS: The other divers and I try not to take ourselves too seriously. We play games such as bouncing like kangaroos upside down under the ice. We also enjoy each other's company. After a long day's hard work we have a good time together back at camp.

The sunken ship *Breadalbane*, showing the ship's wheel

INTERVIEWER: You've been going back to the Arctic at least once a year since 1970. Why?

DR. MacINNIS: The Arctic is one of the last challenges on earth. So I keep returning to it in search of adventure. The challenge is to learn to deal with the ocean and its cover of ice. And the challenge is to test my own limits. Maybe in that way I'm something like a mountain climber. The Arctic ocean is the "Everest" that I want to climb.□

NCE UPON A FABLE...

The Fox and the Grapes

an Aesop fable retold by Anne Terry White

One fine autumn day a Fox was trotting through the woods when the cry of a bird made him look up. What should he see right over his head but a big bunch of purple grapes! The grapes were wild, but quite large and perfectly ripe.

The Fox licked his lips. "Grapes are just the thing for my thirst," he thought.

The grapevine had trailed itself over a high tree branch, and the bunch of grapes hung out of reach. "But they are worth leaping for," the Fox told himself.

So he leaped high with open mouth. It was not quite high enough, though, for his jaws snapped on empty air.

"Well, next time I won't miss," the Fox said. And he leaped again. Once more he came down with nothing.

"I'll try from the other side," the Fox thought. He took a run, leaped, and—missed. Then he tried again. And again. But it was all in vain.

At last the Fox gave up. He turned his back on the grapes and went crossly on his way. "They are probably sour anyway," he said. "I'm sure there isn't a ripe grape among them."

If you cannot get something,
it is easy to say it is no good.

The Boy Who Cried Wolf

an Aesop fable retold by James Reeves

Paul was a shepherd boy who lived in a village not far from a great forest. Every day Paul went out to the fields to mind his master's sheep. There were wolves in that forest, and Paul thought he would play a joke on the people of his village. One day he shouted out at the top of his voice, in a tone of great alarm:

"Wolf! Wolf! Come quickly! The wolf is after my sheep!"

Some of the villagers came rushing out with sticks and stones to drive away the enemy. But when they reached Paul, he was laughing at them.

"How funny you all look!" Paul said. "You're running through the fields with your sticks and stones to frighten away a wolf that isn't here! Oh dear, I shall never stop laughing."

Angrily the villagers returned home. They didn't think Paul's joke was funny at all.

A week or so later the shepherd boy played the same trick. The villagers thought he must really be in trouble this time. Once more they ran to his aid. Once more they found the sheep safe and sound, with not a wolf in sight.

"The boy's a liar," one of the villagers finally said. "He won't get me to come out again with his lying tales!"

A few days later a wolf really did come out of the forest—a big shaggy grey wolf. It ran straight at one of Paul's sheep.

"Wolf! Wolf!" cried Paul, terrified. "Help me, good neighbours, I pray. Help, help!"

But this time the villagers said to each other:

"There's that naughty boy up to his tricks again! But he won't make a fool of us this time."

The villagers took no notice of Paul's shouts. They went on with their work.

With no one to help him, Paul could not drive away the big grey wolf. It pounced upon his sheep and dragged it off into the forest.

Even when liars tell the truth,
people do not believe them.

Maybe, a Mole

by Julia Cunningham

"What foolishness!" said the fox, with a glint in his eye. He was looking at a very small mole, who was stretched as flat as a leaf on top of a large rock. "You belong underground. You will fry your gizzard on that rock."

"That's what I'm hoping will happen," replied the mole in a faint voice. "They don't want me down there."

"Indeed," said the fox. "And why not? Are you stupid or perhaps unwilling to be moleish?"

"Not unwilling. Unable. I am different from the rest. I can see."

The fox pricked up his ears and, for the first time, he looked at the despairing little animal with some respect. "And the others are naturally blind, is that not so?" the fox asked. He smoothed his whiskers thoughtfully. "Why didn't you hide your ability to see?"

The mole raised his pointed head from the rock. "I couldn't. I love to look at things." He slowly sat up. "I would come out of a tunnel at sunset and let the sky dazzle me, then go back and tell them about it. I would — "

"Yes, yes," interrupted the fox. "Let's not cloud the problem with the description of a world I can see very well. What happened, finally?"

"All the moles held a meeting—called it an assembly—and decided to banish me. They threw me out, that's what they did. They simply shoved me from the burrow like a sack of bad roots. Even my brothers and sisters were too ashamed of me to say goodbye."

The fox gazed impatiently at the mole, who was now crying softly. "Why don't you cry for a few minutes and get it over with? Then we can discuss how you can best serve me."

The mole was so astonished that he stopped crying instantly. "Serve you? But why?"

"Because you need a job in the upper world, where you are a stranger. Otherwise you will become a victim. Some animal might make a slave of you forever, if he discovers your gentleness and willingness to please."

"You seem to know me very well already," said the mole shyly, rather comforted by the fox's understanding.

"I do, old friend, I do. I am known to be brilliant." The fox paused to study the mole for a moment. Then he continued, "First I must know your name."

"It's Maybe."

The fox laughed. "May be, might be
Flay me, knight me!"

"There's no need to make fun of me," said the mole

with some dignity. He had left the rock and was seated on the grass in the shade of a dandelion.

"I'm not making fun. Rhymes come to me quite easily. However, back to business, dear Maybe. Climb onto my shoulder. I wish to show you something." The mole obeyed and found a cozy hollow in the soft cinnamon fur of the fox.

"Do you see that rather weary house over the hill?" asked the fox.

"I do," replied the mole, looking at the uneven roof, the peeling paint, and the ragged untended geraniums at each side of the cracked front door.

"It belongs to a most ungenerous man named Sting. He feeds his chickens so little that they're not worth stealing. And he's never been known to give so much as a walnut to a hungry squirrel. Oh, he's happy enough—no need to crinkle up with pity. But the point is, I have heard that he has buried a great treasure somewhere in the ground around his house. And that's where you come in. You will dig for it."

"And if I find it?"

"We'll divide the gold. One share to you, nine shares to me."

"How do you know it is gold?" asked Maybe, who didn't even realize that the bargain was unfair.

"I don't. But what else would be worth burying? How about it? Are you willing?"

"Maybe," said the mole.

"I already know your name," said the fox, who never accepted a weak answer.

The mole smiled. "I'll do it," he said. "You're my friend, and I'll do it."

And so, that very evening when the sun left the sky and the windows of Mr. Sting's house were dark, Maybe began to tunnel. First he tunnelled in a circle around the house. Then, metre by metre, he widened his search. A little before midnight he emerged, very dirty and very tired.

The fox was waiting for him.

"No luck," said Maybe, "except for some grubs I ate for my supper."

"No luck, no pluck," rhymed the fox. When he saw the hurt look in Maybe's eyes, he added hastily, "Oh, don't mind me." He knew that Mr. Sting would see the lines of humped earth around his house in the morning and be on the watch for the mole ever after. This night was their only chance.

"I know what you're thinking," said Maybe.

"Do you?" asked the fox. He was beginning to see that although the mole was not as handsome as a fox, he was just as clever. And intelligence, after all, was of more value.

"Yes," said the mole. "And we've only a few more hours until sunrise, so back I go."

All the rest of that night the mole kept bravely at his search. His paws became so worn with digging that each advance left little tracks of blood in the earth. His breathing was harsh and his back was all one fiery ache. Round and round he went until a circle of earth, as wide as a small lake, had been thoroughly tunnelled. He no longer felt alone. He had found a friend, and he would do his best, as a friend should.

Halfway through his ordeal the mole had found something—a small sack of flat grey seeds. He had eaten a few for strength. Then, to keep himself going, he had tied the sack to his tail so that he could occasionally halt to munch. But it was not until he was ready to go above ground that he noticed the sack had emptied as he worked. He untied it from his tail and poked his head out into the first rays of the rising sun.

In front of him stood the fox, his fur almost scarlet in the new light of day. Maybe collapsed. He had only enough energy left to shake his head sadly before he fell into a deep sleep.

The fox gazed down at the small creature who had so faithfully carried out his part of the bargain. He studied the little animal who had worked all night to please a partner who had planned to cheat him. The fox suddenly realized that the mole was someone to be trusted, to be loved.

Gently the fox lifted Maybe to his back. Then, carrying the mole carefully so as not to disturb his sleep, the fox set off for his den in the far woods.

From that day on the two animals shared their lives. Each gave to the other through a hard, cold winter that arrived too soon and stayed too long. The fox and the mole never went back to Mr. Sting's property. The adventure had become a memory.

But one fine morning the world turned green again and the birds returned to the trees. Maybe packed a picnic lunch and suggested a holiday. "And I'll show you the way," he said.

"We'll never lose, if you choose," the fox agreed.

Maybe was now quite used to his friend's unusual

manner of speaking. He led the way. The fox patiently followed the mole's slow gait.

At noon they came to the border of Mr. Sting's land and suddenly halted in their tracks. The whole hill was blazing with row upon row of giant yellow sunflowers! It was as if the sun itself had descended from the sky and had chosen this field for a visit.

Maybe dropped the picnic basket. The fox sat down hard on his haunches in amazement.

When he had recovered from the first shock of glory, Maybe remembered what had happened the summer before. He told the fox how he had found the seeds and had accidentally scattered them while searching for the treasure.

"But Maybe," said the fox, his eyes as bright as the flowers, "you did find it!"

The mole's mouth began to curve into a smile. "You mean the gold?" he said.

And suddenly, above the hum of the bees and the rustling of the sunflowers, their hilarious laughter rose. They laughed and laughed until they were both flat on their backs, holding their sides. And even that evening, after the fox and mole had eaten their supper and the darkness had come, they had only to look at one another for the peals of laughter to begin again.

Winter's Coming

by Barbara Wilson

Winter's coming.
I can feel it
Pinching all my fingers, toes.

Winter's coming,
I can smell it
Sniffing keenly at my nose.

Winter's coming.
I can hear it.
Icy blasts ring loud and shrill.

Winter's coming.
I can see it.
Frosty world is frozen still.

Winter's coming...
Winter's here.

WINTERSCAPE

Winter Sounds

by S.J. Fitzsimmons

The sounds of winter were different when I was a boy.

Most of all I remember the sounds of sleigh bells as the delivery sleighs made their rounds on silent steel runners that barely crunched through the snow. The jingle-jangle of the bells announced that the stores were making their deliveries on your street. The clip-clopping of the horses' hoofs made a special muffled winter sound that grew louder as the cold grew more intense. You could tell by listening to the jingles whether a single horse was approaching, or a fast-stepping team.

The different breeds of horses also made different sounds from one another. The swift-stepping carriage horses jingled the bells faster than the slow-moving Percherons. And the even slower-moving Clydesdales jingled the bells in a rhythmic double beat.

Today, in winter, footsteps still have the sound of yesterday as they crunch towards you or fade into the distance. But the welcome jingle of the sleigh bells is gone.

Oh yes, the sounds of winter were different when I was a boy. I can still hear them.

Winter Walk in Forest

by George Swede

All else
is so
perfectly still
my breathing sounds
like gusts of wind
my joints
like frozen branches
cracking

All around me
invisible animals
must also be listening

But only
to how close
my boots
snap the snowcrust

Footprints

by Aileen Fisher

In summertime
it's hard to know
where dogs
and mice
and rabbits go:
Their grassy footprints
never show—
you can't tell where
they lead.

In wintertime
there's little doubt
where wild and tame ones
run about:
Their snowy footprints
write it out...
and I know how to read!

Blizzard

by Emily Hearn

The biggest flakes I've ever seen
Are blowing around the sky today.

A million white chrysanthemums,
Whirling in a wild ballet.

Pine trees sway from tangled roots,
The wild wind shrills its horns and flutes.

Nobody walks the streets today,
We're inside, watching the outside play.

Horse Power

It is a cheap source of energy.
It can repair itself.
It can even reproduce itself.
It uses home-grown fuel.
It does not pollute.
Its waste is a valuable energy source, too.
When it is cared for properly,
it will last for 15 to 20 years.

What is this amazing source of power?
It is the horse.

HORSE POWER

Horse Power History

People have used horse power for about five thousand years. Horses have helped people travel and build and pull and carry. The strength, or power, of horses has been used all over the world.

Of course, horses have been around for more than five thousand years. Palaeontologists have studied the fossils of horses. They believe that some kinds of horses lived as long as fifty-five million years ago. The bones and skeletons show that the earliest horses were the size of small dogs. Palaeontologists are still discovering fossils that give new information about early horses.

The earliest horses used by humans seem to have been the wild horses of Mongolia. The people of Mongolia tamed, or domesticated, these horses. They used them in many ways.

In China four thousand years ago, horses were used for herding animals and for other farm work. They were used as pack animals to move loads that people could not carry. They were also used as war horses, carrying soldiers in battles.

War horses were trained to pull chariots. Knights in heavy armour rode huge horses. War horses were developed for their power as well as their speed.

When war horses were not needed in battles, they became work horses. People invented all kinds of coaches and carriages that horses could pull. Stagecoaches were used for long journeys. Sleighs were pulled by teams of horses in winter. Horse power made it possible for people to travel farther and faster than they had ever done before.

Horses delivered mail. Mail coaches were driven from town to town. They worked in relays. When one team of horses was tired out, it stopped and rested. A new team took the mail coach on until it reached another resting place. Then a new team was harnessed up.

Horses were so strong that they could pull barges along canals. Again, the horses worked in relays. There were stations along the canals. At the stations, fresh teams were hitched up, and tired teams were fed and rested. The canals had towpaths beside them for the horses to walk on.

Of course, there were many jobs for horses to do on farms. They pulled ploughs and harvesting machines, as tractors do today. Horses were used for clearing land, pulling down trees, and hauling logs. In Canada in 1921 there were

nine million farmers and almost four million horses. Now most farms have no horses at all because machines do all the work. Some farms still do have horses. Sometimes they are used for work that machines don't do as well. For example, sometimes horses can pull a plough in rough places that a tractor cannot go through without getting stuck. Some farmers, such as the Mennonites, still use horse power instead of machines to do their farm work.

Before automobiles were invented, there were thousands of horses in cities. Sometimes traffic jams of horses and buggies clogged the streets. There were horse-drawn streetcars, taxicabs, and fire engines.

City horses were used to deliver everything from milk to bread to eggs, vegetables, and ice. Most businesses had their own horses and carts. Horses did the work that delivery trucks do now. They carried materials from railways to factories. They hauled loads from the factories to the railways. Just as there are service stations to service cars today, there were blacksmith shops in every town to make and replace iron horseshoes.

Horses made it possible for explorers to cross North America. As people moved west to farm and ranch, cowboys on horseback became important. They worked on the range, herding cattle. They met at round-up times, and would often have competitions to show off their riding and roping skills. Such competitions became known as *rodeos*. The riders and the horses displayed their intelligence, skill, and strength.

North American horses came from different places.

Some were brought by Spaniards to Mexico and the southern United States. Many of these horses wandered around the plains and became wild. Indians who lived on the plains used horses to round up bison. The Blackfoot were probably the first to harness a horse to a *travois*. The travois was a frame of two poles with crossbars. A load could be placed on it and dragged by a horse. The Blackfoot became expert riders. Children as young as seven learned to ride well. Like the cowboys, many Indians became expert at roping and riding.

A special breed of working horses became known as the *Canadian*. Pictures of it were painted by Cornelius Krieghoff. It appears in photographs of early days. Today some horses belonging to the Canadian breed can be seen in Upper Canada Village in Ontario. They appear in parades on special occasions. Five thousand purebred Canadian horses were recorded in 1790. By 1950, however, there were only about two hundred left.

For thousands of years, horses have worked for people. Before machines were invented, the power of the horse made it possible to do many things that machines do today. People have always admired horses for their beauty, their strength, and their intelligence. People have learned how to care for horses and protect them. In return, horses have gone on helping people in many ways.□

Crossing the Creek

by Laura Ingalls Wilder

"Aren't we going to camp pretty soon?" Laura asked. It seemed such a long time since noon, when they had eaten their lunch sitting on the clean grass in the shade of the wagon.

Pa answered: "Not yet. It's too early to camp now."

"I want to camp now! I'm so tired," Laura said.

Then Ma said, "Laura." That was all, but it meant that Laura must not complain. So she did not complain any more out loud, but she was still naughty, inside. She sat and thought complaints to herself.

Laura's legs ached and the wind wouldn't stop blowing her hair. The grass waved and the wagon jolted and nothing else happened for a long time.

"We're coming to a creek or a river," Pa said. "Girls, can you see those trees ahead?"

Laura stood up and held to one of the wagon bows. Far ahead she saw a low dark smudge. "That's trees," Pa said. "You can tell by the shape of the shadows. In this country, trees mean water. That's where we'll camp tonight."

The mustangs, Pet and Patty, began to trot briskly, as if they were glad, too. Laura held tightly to the wagon bow and stood up in the jolting wagon. Beyond Pa's shoulder and far across the waves of green grass she could see the trees, and they were not like any trees she had seen before. They were no taller than bushes.

"Whoa!" said Pa, suddenly. "Now which way?" he muttered to himself.

The road divided here, and you could not tell which was the more-travelled way. Both of them were faint wheel tracks in the grass. One went towards the west, the other sloped downwards a little, towards the south. Both soon vanished in the tall, blowing grass.

"Better go downhill, I guess," Pa decided. "The creek's down in the bottoms. Must be this is the way to the ford." He turned Pet and Patty towards the south.

The road went down and up and down and up again, over gently curving land. The trees were nearer now, but they were no taller. Then Laura gasped and clutched the wagon bow, for almost under Pet's and Patty's noses there was no more blowing grass. There was no land at all. She looked beyond the edge of the land and across the tops of trees.

The road turned there. For a little way it went along the cliff's top, then it went sharply downwards. Pa put on the brakes; Pet and Patty braced themselves backwards and almost sat down. The wagon wheels slid onward, little by little lowering the wagon farther down the steep slope into the ground. Jagged cliffs of bare red earth rose on both sides of the wagon. Grass waved along their tops, but nothing grew on their seamed, straight-up-and-down sides. The cliffs were hot, and heat came from them against Laura's face. The wind was still blowing overhead, but it did not blow down into this deep crack in the ground. The stillness seemed strange and empty.

Then once more the wagon was level. The narrow crack down which it had come opened into the bottom lands. Here grew the tall trees whose tops Laura had seen from the prairie above. Shady groves were scattered on the rolling meadows, and in the groves deer were lying down, hardly to be seen among the shadows. The deer turned their heads towards the wagon, and curious fawns stood up to see it more clearly.

Laura was surprised because she did not see the creek. But the bottom lands were wide. Down here, below the prairie, there were gentle hills and open sunny places. The air was still and hot. Under the wagon wheels the ground was soft. In the sunny open spaces the grass grew thin, and deer had cropped it short.

For a while the high, bare cliffs of red earth stood up behind the wagon. But they were almost hidden behind hills and trees when Pet and Patty stopped to drink from the creek.

The rushing sound of the water filled the still air. All along the creek banks the trees hung over it and made it dark with shadows. In the middle it ran swiftly, sparkling silver and blue.

"This creek's pretty high," Pa said. "But I guess we can make it all right. You can see this is a ford, by the old wheel ruts. What do you say, Caroline?"

"Whatever you say, Charles," Ma answered.

Pet and Patty lifted their wet noses. They pricked their ears forward, looking at the creek; then they pricked them backwards to hear what Pa would say. They sighed and laid their soft noses together to whisper to each other. A little way upstream, Jack was lapping the water with his red tongue.

"I'll tie down the wagon-cover," Pa said. He climbed down from the seat, unrolled the canvas sides, and tied them firmly to the wagon box. Then he pulled the rope at the back so that the canvas puckered together in the middle, leaving only a tiny round hole, too small to see through.

Mary huddled down on the bed. She did not like fords; she was afraid of the rushing water. But Laura was excited; she liked the splashing. Pa climbed to the seat, saying, "They may have to swim, out there in the middle. But we'll make it all right, Caroline."

Laura thought of Jack and said, "I wish Jack could ride in the wagon, Pa."

Pa did not answer. He gathered the reins tightly in his hands. Ma said, "Jack can swim, Laura. He's a strong dog. He will be all right."

The wagon went forward softly in mud. Water began to splash against the wheels. The splashing grew louder. The wagon shook as the noisy water struck at it. Then all at once the wagon lifted and balanced and swayed. It was a lovely feeling.

The noise stopped, and Ma said sharply, "Lie down, girls!"

Quick as a flash, Mary and Laura dropped flat on the bed. When Ma spoke like that, they did as they were told. Ma's arm pulled a smothering blanket over them, heads and all.

"Be still, just as you are. Don't move!" she said.

Mary did not move; she was trembling and still. But Laura could not help wriggling a little bit. She did so want to see what was happening. She could feel the wagon swaying and turning; the splashing was noisy again, and again it died away. Then Pa's voice frightened Laura. It said, "Take them, Caroline!"

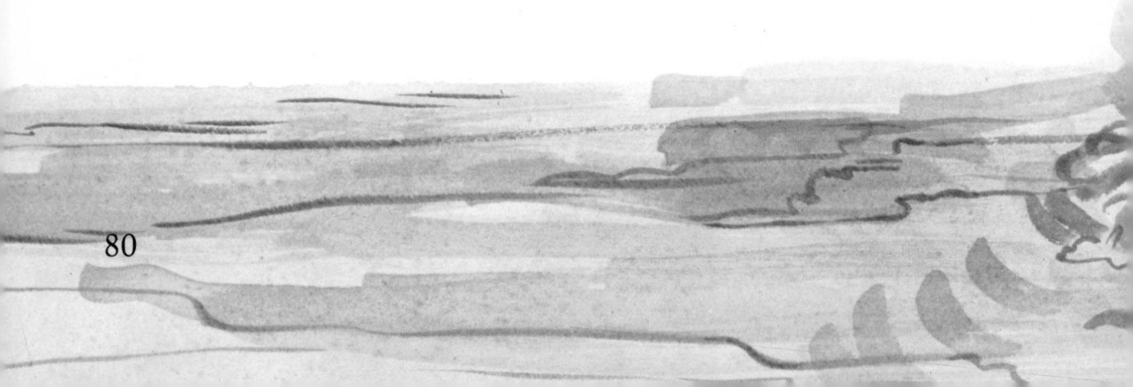

The wagon lurched; there was a sudden heavy splash beside it. Laura sat straight up and clawed the blanket from her head.

Pa was gone. Ma sat alone, holding tight to the reins with both hands. Mary hid her face in the blanket again, but Laura rose up farther. She couldn't see the creek bank. She couldn't see anything in front of the wagon but water rushing at it. And in the water, three heads: Pet's head and Patty's head and Pa's small, wet head. Pa's fist in the water was holding tightly to Pet's bridle.

Laura could faintly hear Pa's voice through the rushing of the water. It sounded calm and cheerful, but she couldn't hear what he said. He was talking to the horses. Ma's face was white and scared.

"Lie down, Laura," Ma said.

Laura lay down. She felt cold and sick. Her eyes were shut tight, but she could still see the terrible water and Pa's brown beard drowning in it.

For a long, long time the wagon swayed and swung, and Mary cried without making a sound, and Laura's stomach felt sicker and sicker. Then the front wheels struck and grated, and Pa shouted. The whole wagon jerked and jolted and tipped backwards, but the wheels were turning on the ground. Laura was up again, holding to the seat; she saw Pet's and Patty's scrambling wet backs climbing a steep bank, and Pa running beside them, shouting, "Hi, Patty! Hi, Pet! Get up! Get up! Whoopsy-daisy! Good girls!"

At the top of the bank they stood still, panting and dripping. And the wagon stood still, safely out of that creek.

Pa stood panting and dripping, too, and Ma said, "Oh, Charles!"

"There, there, Caroline," said Pa. "We're all safe, thanks to a good tight wagon-box well fastened to the running-gear. I never saw a creek rise so fast in my life. Pet and Patty are good swimmers, but I guess they wouldn't have made it if I hadn't helped them."

If Pa had not known what to do, or if Laura and Mary had been naughty and bothered Ma while she drove, then they would all have been lost. The river would have rolled them over and over and carried them away and drowned them, and nobody would ever have known what became of them. For weeks, perhaps, no other person would come along that road.

"Well," said Pa, "all's well that ends well," and Ma said, "Charles, you're wet to the skin."

Before Pa could answer, Laura cried, "Oh, where's Jack?"

They had forgotten Jack. They had left him on the other side of that dreadful water, and now they could not see him anywhere. He must have tried to swim after them, but they could not see him struggling in the water now.

Laura swallowed hard, to keep from crying. . . . Jack had followed them so patiently and faithfully, and now they had left him to drown. He was so tired, and they might have taken him into the wagon. He had stood on the bank and seen the wagon going away from him, as if they didn't care for him at all. And he would never know how much they wanted him.

Pa said he wouldn't have done such a thing to Jack, not for a million dollars. If he'd known how that creek would rise when they were in midstream, he would never have let Jack try to swim it. "But that can't be helped now," he said.

He went far up and down the creek bank, looking for Jack, calling him and whistling for him.

It was no use. Jack was gone.

At last there was nothing to do but to go on. Pet and Patty were rested. Pa's clothes had dried on him while he searched for Jack. He took the reins again and drove uphill to the high prairie.

Purple shadows were gathering over the land, and the wind was mourning. Pa stopped the mustangs. He and Ma got out of the wagon, and Mary and Laura climbed down to the ground, too.

Pa made camp as usual. First he unhitched and unharnessed Pet and Patty, and he put them on their picket-lines. Picket-lines were long ropes fastened to iron pegs driven into the ground. The pegs were called picket-pins. When horses were on picket-lines they could eat all the grass that the long ropes would let them reach. But when Pet and Patty were put on them, the first thing they did was to lie down and roll back and forth and over. They rolled till the feeling of the harness was all gone from their backs.

While Pet and Patty were rolling, Pa pulled all the grass from a large, round space of ground. There was old, dead grass at the roots of the green grass, and Pa would take no chance of setting the prairie on fire. If fire once started in that dry under-grass, it would sweep the whole country bare and black. Pa said, "Best be on the safe side; it saves trouble in the end."

When the space was clear of grass, Pa laid a handful of dry grass in its centre. From the creek bottoms he brought an armful of twigs and dead wood. He laid small twigs and larger twigs and then the wood on the handful of dry grass, and he lighted the grass. The fire crackled merrily inside the ring of bare ground that it couldn't get out of.

Then Pa brought water from the creek while Mary and Laura helped Ma get supper.

While they were eating supper, the purple shadows closed around the camp fire. The vast prairie was dark and still. Only the wind moved stealthily through the grass, and the large, low stars hung glittering from the great sky. In the dark beyond the wagon, Pet and Patty were eating, too. They bit off bites of grass with sharply crunching sounds.

After supper, Pa lighted his pipe with a hot coal, and

stretched out his legs comfortably. Mary yawned, and slid off the wagon tongue to sit on the grass. Laura yawned, too.

"Bedtime for little girls!" Ma said, cheerfully. Mary got up and turned around so that Ma could unbutton her. But Laura jumped up and stood still. She saw something. Deep in the dark beyond the firelight, two green lights were shining near the ground. They were eyes.

Cold ran up Laura's backbone. Her scalp crinkled. Her hair stood up. The green lights moved; one winked out, then the other winked out, then both shone steadily, coming nearer. Very rapidly they were coming nearer.

"Look, Pa, look!" Laura said. "A wolf!"

Pa did not seem to move quickly, but he did. In an instant he took his gun out of the wagon and was ready to fire at those green eyes. The eyes stopped coming. They were still in the dark, looking at him.

"It can't be a wolf. Unless it's a mad wolf," Pa said. Ma lifted Mary into the wagon. "And it's not that," said Pa. "Listen to the horses." Pet and Patty were still biting off bits of grass.

"A lynx?" said Ma.

"Or a coyote?" Pa picked up a stick of wood; he shouted, and threw it. The green eyes went close to the ground, as if the animal crouched to spring. Pa held the gun ready. The creature did not move.

"Don't, Charles," Ma said. But Pa slowly walked towards those eyes. And slowly along the ground the eyes crawled towards him. Laura could see the animal in the edge of the dark. It was a tawny animal and brindled. Then Pa shouted and Laura screamed.

The next thing she knew she was trying to hug a jumping, panting, wriggling Jack, who lapped her face and hands with his warm wet tongue. She couldn't hold him. He leaped and wriggled from her to Pa to Ma and back to her again.

Jack was perfectly well. But soon he lay down close to Laura and sighed a long sigh. His eyes were red with tiredness, and all the under part of him was caked with mud. Ma gave him a cornmeal cake and he licked it and wagged politely, but he could not eat. He was too tired.

"No telling how long he kept swimming," Pa said. "Nor how far he was carried downstream before he landed." And when at last he reached them, Laura called him a wolf, and Pa threatened to shoot him.

But Jack knew they didn't mean it. Laura asked him, "You knew we didn't mean it, didn't you, Jack?" Jack wagged his stump of a tail; he knew.

It was past bedtime. Pa chained Pet and Patty to the feed-box at the back of the wagon and fed them their corn. Under the wagon, Jack wearily turned around three times, and lay down to sleep.

In the wagon, Laura and Mary said their prayers and crawled into their little bed. Ma kissed them good night.

On the other side of the canvas, Pet and Patty were eating their corn. When Patty whooshed into the feedbox, the whoosh was right at Laura's ear. There were little scurrying sounds in the grass. In the trees by the creek an owl called, "Who-oo? who-oo?" Farther away another owl answered, "Oo-oo, oo-oo." Far away on the prairie the wolves howled, and under the wagon Jack growled low in his chest. In the wagon everything was safe and snug.

Thickly in front of the open wagon-top hung the large, glittering stars. Pa could reach them, Laura thought. She wished he would pick the largest one from the thread on which it hung from the sky, and give it to her. She was wide awake, she was not sleepy at all, but suddenly she was very much surprised. The large star winked at her!

Then she was waking up, next morning.□

Horses in the Coal Mines

by Ron Caplan

Horses have worked above ground in fields and forests, in cities and towns. Horses have also worked underground. In the days when nearly everyone used coal or wood for heating and cooking, horses helped miners pull loads of coal out of Nova Scotia mines. Miners agree that the work could not have been done successfully without these powerful helpers.

There are still people in Nova Scotia today who worked with horses in the mines. They remember what it was like. In the accounts that follow, three Nova Scotia miners describe their memories.

Bert Gouthro, from Glace Bay, was a driver when he first worked in the mines. "The men's livelihood depended on the horses—certainly it did—to haul their coal," says Bert.

Bert worked with a horse and a four-wheeled *coal box*. The coal box travelled on rails like a train. It held 1 t to 1.5 t of coal. The horse would haul an empty box through underground passages to a coal *face* where miners were digging the coal. The miners would fill the box. Then the horse would haul the loaded box back to the *landing*, where it was raised to the surface and emptied. When the empty box was lowered to the landing again, horse and driver set off to collect the next load.

Bert Gouthro

How much a driver was paid depended on the amount of coal he and his horse hauled, and how far they hauled it. The most a driver could earn was about seventeen cents per tonne.

Bert cared about the horses he worked with. He says that other men were close to their horses, too.

"One particular time I got a new horse, a young horse," Bert remembers, "and believe me, I got attached to that little horse. He must have been five or six years old, and he could pull like a little tractor. I was what they call 'hauling off from a chain.' I was hauling three or four boxes joined together. That horse would get right down, and you could see him feeling with his feet to get footing, you know. I'd just stand alongside of him, and he'd straighten out to get those four boxes moving. And the only thing I ever hit him with in my life was my glove.

"Then one day, when I wasn't there, the horse worked with another driver. He was badly injured and he died.

Even the loaders, the men who were loading the coal for me, they felt bad about it. Oh yes, some of the drivers were very attached to their horses. And then—like everything else—there were others who didn't care at all."

Most of the horses that worked in the mines were born in the Atlantic provinces. Some of the horses were ponies—small horses. Ponies were often used in passages where the sides were narrow and the ceilings were low. Full-sized horses worked in passages where there was more space.

Hauling coal was difficult, dangerous work. The horses had to be sure-footed and strong. They had to keep their heads down so that they wouldn't bump into low ceilings. They had to step over holes in the ground and the pieces of wood that held the railway tracks in place. The underground passages led up and down hills. When the horses walked uphill they had to pull their loads behind them. When they plodded downhill they had to brace themselves so that the weight of their loads wouldn't topple them over. Careful drivers helped their horses through dangerous places and tried to keep them safe, but there were many accidents.

Patrick McNeil, also from Glace Bay, worked with a veterinarian to take care of horses injured in the mines.

"I spent most of my life working around horses at the Veterinary Horse Hospital in the Sterling Yard," recalls Patrick. "I worked as an assistant to Dr. John L. Sullivan, the first veterinarian. I had no special training. But when you work with a vet, you learn from day to day what to do, and you get a pretty fair knowledge, like any other job.

"Dr. Sullivan came to the coal field about 1920, and he devoted all his time to the betterment of horses. One

Patrick McNeil

of the best things Dr. Sullivan did was to build a horse hospital out in the Sterling Yard. And that hospital had an operating table. It was a piece of heavy hardwood, and he would tip it up straight. Then we would put the horse alongside of it. There were straps to go on the four legs, and two girths would go around the body and draw the horse right in tight to the table. Then the table would crank down and the doctor would operate. Sometimes it would be broken bones or a deep wound that he couldn't get at otherwise. We would give the horse an anesthetic. It was very humane."

Patrick helped Dr. Sullivan to treat many horses. Even without injury, he says, it was a hard life for a horse.

"The horse was fed well and he was cared for, you might say. But when they hired a young fellow to work in the mines, maybe he didn't know the front end of a horse from the back end. And that's the first job he got, was driving a horse. The carelessness of new drivers caused many an accident...that and just plain ignorance."

Archie MacDonald

Archie MacDonald, from Florence, tells about a strong head stableman who taught drivers to take proper care of their horses.

"In the afternoon and evening, when the horses would be coming in, this big husky fellow would watch them, looking for any bruises or scrapes or anything like that. And if he saw any injury, he'd stop the driver. 'Just a minute, I want to have a look at that,' he'd say. 'How did it happen?' And the driver had to have a good answer, or the first thing he knew, the fellow would have him by the throat and want to know how it happened. None of the drivers was tough enough to stand up to this fellow. And I bet you in three months, three months or less, the horses were in spick-and-span condition.

"That's a true story. That fellow lived to be an old man. He retired. But he loved horses. And he could not tolerate in any way, shape, or form a driver who abused his horse. He retrained the drivers. He surely did. Nobody'd tackle a horse or damage a horse while this fellow was on."

Patrick McNeil says that in the early days the horses lived entirely in stables underground and never came out of the mines.

"A horse went down into the mine and stayed there year in and year out, if he lasted that long," says Patrick. "And he never saw daylight till back, I guess, in the '40s. When the miners started getting vacations, they started taking the horses up. And the horses really enjoyed it when they'd get into the fields.

"As soon as they'd hit that field, you could see them race from one end to the other and kick their heels in the air. Really, they enjoyed it. They'd be a little, likely, sun-blind when they'd come out at first, from being in the dark so long. But they'd soon adapt to the daylight. I remember lots of times they'd be coming out of the pit, and there'd be a puddle. They'd jump. They weren't used to seeing that, you know, a little puddle on the road. They were skittish, because in the pit all they saw was what was ahead of them. But they managed very well.

"It was back in the '40s also that the companies started to mechanize the mines. New Waterford was the first district to go horseless. Then it gradually kept coming along. And then about 1960 the last horse was out of the mine. And now there are none."

This is Fraser, the last of the horses to serve in 1B Mine. The photograph was taken in 1955 at the time of his retirement. Fraser spent more of his life underground than any other horse in the company's history. In this picture, Fraser may serve to represent all the horses who worked in the coal mines of Nova Scotia, helping the miners haul their coal.□

The Pit Ponies

by Leslie Norris

They come like the ghosts of horses, shyly,
To this summer field, this fresh green,
Which scares them.

They have been too long in the blind mine,
Their hoofs have trodden only stones
And the soft, thick dust of fine coal,

And they do not understand the grass.
For over two years their sun
Has shone from an electric bulb

That has never set, and their walking
Has been along the one, monotonous
Track of the piled coal trucks.

They have bunched their muscles against
The harness, and pulled and hauled.
But now they have come out of the underworld

And are set down in the sun and real air,
Which are strange to them. They are humble
And modest, their heads are downcast, they

Do not attempt to see very far. But one
Is attempting a clumsy gallop. It is
Something he could do when he was very young,

When he was a little foal a long time ago
And could run fleetly on his long foal's legs,
And almost he can remember this. And look,

One rolls on her back with joy in the clean grass!
And they all, awkwardly and hesitantly, like
Clumsy old men, begin to run, and the field

Is full of happy thunder. They toss their heads,
Their manes fly, they are galloping in freedom.
The ponies have come above ground, they are galloping!

ACE ASSOCIATES, INC.
PRIVATE INVESTIGATIONS
MISSING PERSONS—IF THEY'RE LOS
WE'LL FIND THEM
65 Dingbell Lane 111-500
BLACKIE, B.
PRIVATE EYE
20 YEARS EXPERIENCE
13 Crookedtree Street 110-29
FIRST CLASS FACTFINDERS
CRIMINAL INVESTIGATORS
LIE DETECTOR TESTS
4000 Pickpocket Place ...106-66
GOOD LUCK SERVICES
OVER 50 YEARS EXPERIENCE
CALL US FIRST
.......123-1313

CALLING ALL DETECTIVES

HOLMES, HEADLOCK
PRIVATE INVESTIGATOR
"IF I CAN'T SOLVE THE CASE, NO ONE CAN"
221-B Sleuth Street 191-2965

HYDE AND SEEK ASSOCIATES
UNDERCOVER INVESTIGATION
709 Blanket Avenue 171-7171

PROBE AND PEEK INVESTIGATORS

PHOTOGRAPHIC SERVICES

OPEN NIGHT AND DAY

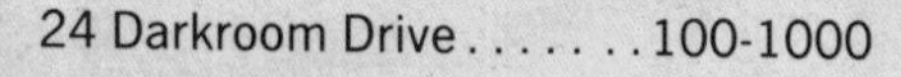
24 Darkroom Drive 100-1000

SLEUTHWORKS, INC.
SECURITY CONSULTANTS
NO JOB TOO SMALL
111 Shady Alley 132-3211

SMOOTH, SAM
THE BEST IN THE BUSINESS
100 Tumbledown Street . . 123-1234

TOUGH, TRICKY & CROOK
SECURITY INVESTIGATORS
A NAME YOU CAN TRUST
P.O. Box I.C. Station O 156-7354

WORLDWIDE INVESTIGATIONS
VANCOUVER, LONDON, HONG KONG
"FOR INFORMATION CALL"
RICK SHAW
10001 Threadneedle Street
100-14-2-189-7865

ZED, XAVIER
MASTER DETECTIVE
THE LAST WORD IN INVESTIGATORS
24-HOUR SERVICE
999 Picklock Court 189-7899

The Secret of the Fortune Cookie

by Ricki Glinert

"So you want to be a detective, kid?" Sam asked, looking straight into my eyes.

"Yes, Mr. Smooth," I said. "That's why I've come to you. You're the best detective there is, and I thought maybe you would teach me."

"Well, kid, I'd like to help," Sam said as he munched some chow mein. "But I'm too busy right now to teach anybody anything."

"Perhaps I could follow you around a bit and just watch?" I asked. I had already followed the great Sam Smooth into the Chinese restaurant where he was having lunch.

"You know, kid, being a detective isn't an easy job." Sam spoke slowly, shifting his cool, steady gaze to the fortune cookie sitting on his plate. "Crimes don't just drop into your lap," he added as he opened the fortune cookie. The fortune floated down onto Sam's lap. "You can go for weeks without having a case to solve."

"I know that," I said. "I just thought——"

"Very strange," interrupted Sam.

"What is it?" I asked.

"A crime," Sam replied. "It just dropped into my lap."

"That's just your fortune from the cookie," I said. "All fortune cookies have little pieces of paper with messages written on them."

"But not like this one," Sam said.

I read the message:

"I think that's a joke I heard once," I said to Mr. Smooth.

"This is no joke," said Sam, reaching for his well-worn trenchcoat. "This is your chance to be a detective. It looks as if we've got ourselves a crime to solve." Sam was in such a hurry to get on the case that he forgot to pay for his lunch.

I paid Sam's bill and followed him out of the restaurant, thrilled to see the famous cool-headed detective in action. Sam led me to a big grey building. We went in.

"This could be dangerous, kid," Sam whispered. "This is the Luck Fortune Cookie Factory. Whoever sent that message is probably inside."

"I'm not scared," I lied.

"You have no reason to be scared," said a strange voice behind us. Quickly we turned around, ready for action. There stood a well-dressed man.

"I am Mr. Luck. I own this factory. What can I do for you?"

Sam showed Mr. Luck the note.

"I believe this note came from your factory," he said, casually smoothing a wrinkle in his trenchcoat.

"Many factories use fortune cookie messages that look just like this one," replied Mr. Luck. "You might be a clever detective, Sam Smooth, but you have no proof that this message came from my factory. Good-bye."

Mr. Luck helped us out the door.

"Well, Mr. Smooth, what do we do now?" I asked.

"We consult another detective," said Sam Smooth. "That's what detectives do all the time. We just don't tell too many people about it. And I know a really great detective."

"Who's that?" I asked.

"Headlock Holmes," Sam answered.

"I think I've seen an old movie about him," I said.

"That's not the same Headlock Holmes," said Mr. Smooth.

Soon we were in the office of Headlock Holmes, private investigator.

"Sam Smooth," Holmes smiled. "So good to see you again, old chap."

"This is the Kid," Sam said, introducing me.

"Jolly good to meet you, Kid. Now what can I do for you, Sam Smooth?"

Sam told him about our case.

"Interesting indeed," Holmes replied. "There appear to be many crumbs to this cookie. All the restaurants in town buy from the Luck Company. And this is definitely the kind of paper they use for their fortunes. Whoever wrote that message must be in their factory."

"But how do we get into the factory?" I asked.

"Come, I will show you," Holmes said. He led us through a door at the back of his office to a small room filled with large vases.

"Here's the plan. Sam, you hide in one of these vases. The Kid hides in the other. Then we deliver the vases to the factory. Mr. Luck thinks they are a gift and takes them into his office. When he goes home for the night, you get out of the vases and find the note writer."

"Splendid idea, Holmes! Thank you," Sam said. It was the first time I'd seen Mr. Smooth excited.

"I think I've read about that idea," I said. "It was in a story called *Ali Baba and the Forty Thieves*. It didn't work."

Nevertheless, Sam and I climbed into the vases, and Holmes delivered them to the factory. I could hear Mr. Luck praising the wonderful gift. He thanked Headlock. Then he closed the factory. Soon all was quiet.

"Kid," I heard Sam whisper. "No one is here. Let's get out of the vases and look around."

We got out as easily as we had got in, which wasn't very easily. We were in the main office of the factory.

"Well, Mr. Smooth, where do we start looking?" I asked.

Suddenly we heard a muffled tapping. It seemed to be coming from a closet at the far end of the office. Sam rushed to the closet, picked the lock with his nail file, and opened the door. The closet wasn't a closet at all. It was really the entrance to a secret passage that led downstairs. We followed the passage to another door. Once again, Sam opened it with his trusty nail file. In the room sat a young woman.

"Are you a prisoner in this cookie factory? Did you write that fortune?" Sam asked.

"Yes, it was the only way I could get a message out of here," replied the woman.

"Who are you?" I asked.

"I'm detective Sue Clark," she answered. "I got a job in the Luck Factory putting messages into fortune

cookies. I came here so that I could check out Mr. Luck. But I asked too many questions and ended up here. Mr. Luck said I knew too much. That's why he locked me up."

"What do you know?" Sam asked.

"All kinds of things," said Sue Clark. "For example, there are only twelve different fortunes in all the cookies. That's cheap. And the hundred-year-old eggs were laid last week. That's crooked."

"But they *look* a hundred years old," said Sam.

"That's because Mr. Luck has wrinkles painted on them. He sells them for a hundred dollars each at the Chinese New Year's feast. I intend to expose Mr. Luck. His luck is about to run out."

"The New Year's feast is tonight," said Sam. "What a coincidence. Let's go."

Sam and Sue and I grabbed a taxicab and rushed to the feast. We stopped along the way so that Sam could buy a real hundred-year-old egg. When we arrived, we saw Mr. Luck and his helpers setting up their own display of wrinkled eggs.

Sam strolled up to Mr. Luck.

"Those eggs are phony," he said with no expression in his voice.

"They are a hundred years old," Mr. Luck insisted.

"They are not," said Sam. "Kid, roll this egg along the table."

I took Sam's egg and pushed it. The egg moved only slightly.

"That is a hundred-year-old egg," Mr. Luck said.

"That's right," Sam said. "It's my egg. Now, kid, take one of Mr. Luck's eggs and roll it."

I took one of the wrinkled eggs and pushed it. The egg rolled quickly down the table.

"That's a new egg," Sam said. "Kid, call the police."

"But, Mr. Smooth, how can you tell?" I asked.

"Hundred-year-old eggs are too old to move very quickly or very far, but new eggs are full of get-up-and-go." Sam pushed the two eggs again to show me. "We've caught you, Mr. Luck, and that's the way the cookie crumbles. I mean, that's the way the egg rolls."

"Wow, I wish I could say things like that," I said.

"But it's not my fault," protested Mr. Luck. "I didn't mean to do it. It was my brother's idea."

"You have no brother, and you're not Mr. Luck. The game's up!" said Headlock Holmes as he leaped out from behind the display. He quickly pulled a tight rubber mask from Mr. Luck's face.

Sam gasped. "Why, it's the infamous criminal Nitcross Twit, often called the Nit Twit." Sam was so excited that he almost lost his cool.

"And I'm not really Sue Clark," said the woman detective as she too peeled a tight rubber mask off her face. "I'm Sue Luck. This Nit Twit man has been trying to destroy my father's good reputation. Ever since my father became ill, Mr. Twit has been posing as my dad. He's been making a lot of fake stuff to ruin my father's business."

"Hey!" I shouted. "Then he could buy the business cheap!"

"You're a smart kid," said Sam, calmly buttoning his beat-up old trenchcoat. "You'll make a great detective some day. But for now, what if you and I go around the corner to a little pizza place where you can buy me a snack."

"Sure, Sam. Anything you say," I replied as we watched Sue and Headlock Holmes marching Mr. Twit off to the police station. "Maybe another crime will fall into your lap."☐

Adapted from a story by Ricki Glinert

On the Trail of the Missing Bike

by Allen Morgan

Wednesday was John's tenth birthday. His father and mother gave him a twenty-dollar bill and a ten-speed bicycle. John called up his best friend, Mike, right after dinner and told him all about it.

"Wait till you see my bike," John said. "It's got quick-release wheels and double brake handles so you can brake from the top of the handle bars."

"Sounds really decent," agreed Mike.

"It's better than decent," said John. "It's excellent."

Then John called Ben and Sally and told them the same thing.

It rained on Thursday. John couldn't ride his new bike to school, so he went downtown that afternoon and bought a horn instead. And a speedometer. And a raccoon tail. Mike came over to help him put the new equipment onto his bike.

"I'm glad I waited to buy this extra stuff before I brought the bike to school," said John when they were finished. "When the other kids see it, they'll turn green with envy."

But as it turned out, it was John who turned a little green. Friday morning when he went outside to get on his bike, it was gone. Someone had stolen it during the night. The chain had been neatly snipped just above the lock.

John's father called the police station. When the police arrived, they took down a description of the missing bike. But they warned John that the bike would be very difficult, and maybe impossible, to find. So John called a meeting of his detective club. When the club met after breakfast on Saturday morning, all the detectives were sure they could crack the case.

"Easy as pie," said Mike.

Ben nodded. "We'll have those crooks behind bars before supper," he said.

"They'll be sorry they ever touched that bike of yours," vowed Sally. "They've got the Barton Avenue Detectives on their trail now, and the kids from B.A.D. always solve the crime."

"All right," said John. "Everybody spread out. Keep your eyes open for anybody acting suspicious and report back here at noon. Mom's going to make sandwiches. Ready? Let's roll!"

The Barton Avenue Detectives were off and rolling, but they didn't have much luck right away. John and Mike were the first to report back for lunch at quarter to twelve.

"Did you see anything?" asked John.

"No luck," replied Mike.

"I didn't see anything, either," said John.

Just then Ben arrived, shaking his head sadly.

"Maybe Sally saw something," said Ben.

"I bet she struck out just like us," said John.

But John was wrong about that. When Sally came running up to the porch a few minutes later, she had big news.

"I saw them," she cried. "I saw them!"

"The bike thieves?" asked John.

"I think so. I saw a blue van going down the street very slowly," explained Sally. "It kept stopping and going, and then stopping again. The thing was, it stopped in front of all the houses that had bicycles parked out front."

"Terrific!" cried John. "Sounds like the thieves all right. They must be casing the neighbourhood for likely places to hit later on."

"Then they'll come back at night," said Ben, thinking ahead.

"Exactly," said John. "Did you get the licence number of the van?"

"I couldn't get close enough," said Sally. "I was just sneaking up on the van when it took off around the block."

"It's probably still around somewhere," suggested Mike.

"I hope so," said John. "We'll go partners this time. Mike, you and Ben take the west side of the neighbourhood, and Sally and I will do the east side. Come on, let's not waste any time."

A short while later John and Sally were doing foot patrol on a quiet street when Sally spotted the blue van cruising slowly down the block ahead.

"There it is!" Sally cried, grabbing John's arm.

"After it!" shouted John, and they took off in hot pursuit.

The van was going so slowly that John and Sally easily caught up. They hid behind a tree when it stopped at the curb about halfway down the block.

"Write down the licence number," whispered John. "I'm going to sneak closer to see who's inside." He crept along behind some parked cars until he was right across the street from the van. He saw two men in the front seat. While the driver pointed to a bicycle on a nearby porch, the second man wrote something down in a little book. Then both men laughed, and the van pulled away from the curb. It continued down the street.

"They're the crooks sure enough," John told Sally when she caught up with him. "They're planning another raid. Let's keep them in sight."

John and Sally followed the van as it drove slowly around the block. But just when their luck seemed to be improving, it turned bad again. The van turned back onto the main street and pulled out into heavy traffic.

"Hey, they're getting away!" cried John.

"Quick, let's phone the police," said Sally. "We know their van now, and we even have the licence number. The police could pick them up for us, no trouble."

But when Sally and John got to a telephone booth, it was out of order. There was no other phone booth in sight, and the blue van was already halfway down the block.

"Come on, we'll have to follow them ourselves," shouted John, and he started running down the sidewalk. Luckily there was a taxicab parked near by. Sally spotted it and jumped into the back seat. John jumped in right behind her.

"Follow that van!" he told the cabdriver breathlessly.

The cabdriver turned around and stared at him. "You must be kidding," he said.

"He's not," replied Sally. "Hurry, we don't want to lose them!"

"I've been driving this cab for fifteen years," said the cabdriver. "And not once has anyone ever told me to 'follow that car.'"

"*Van*," insisted Sally. "Come on, it's getting away."

"You kids have been watching too much TV," the cabdriver continued. "Come on now, out of the cab, and no fooling around. I'm working."

"But we can pay," protested John, pulling out the twenty-dollar bill his parents had given him for his birthday.

The cabdriver looked at the green bill for a moment. Then he shrugged. "Your money, your cab," he said, turning on the meter. "Fifteen years and I thought I'd heard everything. 'Follow that car.' Who'd believe it?"

As the cabdriver pulled out into the street, he picked up the radio mike and called in to his dispatcher.

"This is car forty-three," he said.

"Go ahead, four-three," answered the radio.

"I've picked up a flag and I'm going to zone eight."

"Right, four-three. Red-two, you're first now."

Sitting on the edge of their seat, John and Sally peered through the front windshield for a glimpse of the blue van. When they finally saw it, about a block away, they both groaned. The crooks were pulling farther and farther ahead in the traffic, and the cab-driver didn't seem very concerned about staying close behind.

"You two look a little young to be police officers," he said, making conversation.

"We're detectives," explained Sally.

"Barton Avenue Detectives," said John. "I'm the chief."

"I'm the assistant chief," said Sally.

"And I'm the minister of transport," chuckled the cabdriver. "I bet that van's full of money from a bank hold-up, right?"

"Stolen bicycles," said John, and he explained the case.

"Sounds as if you might be on to something," admitted the cabdriver. "Stolen bike ring, eh? My boy's bike was taken two weeks ago. You think these guys had something to do with it?"

After that the cabdriver gave all his attention to staying on the tail of the blue van. He almost lost it a few times in heavy traffic, but he was right behind when the van turned into a driveway on the other side of town. The cabdriver pulled over to the curb a half-block away. The meter read $7.50. John gave the cabdriver the twenty-dollar bill and told him to drive around the block.

"Hold on a minute," said the cabdriver. "I can't do that."

"Isn't twenty dollars enough to hold the cab?" asked John.

"More than enough," said the cabdriver. "But I don't like the idea of you kids messing around with those robbers."

"We can take care of ourselves," said John. "We're detectives."

"We aren't going to *do* anything," Sally assured the cabdriver. "We're just going to look in the window to see if we've got the right place. They won't even notice us."

The cabdriver thought for a moment.

"I'm going to stay parked outside just to make sure," he said at last.

"They might see you waiting and get suspicious," said John. "If they get nervous, they might just take off."

"Well, OK," sighed the cabdriver. "I'll go around the block. But you two better be here when I get back. Just one peek in the window and that's all. I don't want you getting hurt."

John and Sally got out of the cab and watched it move slowly down the block. Then they crept along the side of the house to the back corner. They peeked around the corner and into the rear window. The two men were there all right.

They were drinking coffee and studying a city street map. The smaller man traced a path down the map with his finger while the other, who was much larger, made some notes in his little book.

"Let's call the police now," whispered Sally.

"We don't have any real proof yet," John whispered back. "We have to find out where they're keeping the bikes."

Looking back along the side of the house, John noticed some steps leading down to a basement door. He pointed them out to Sally. They both went to investigate. The door at the bottom was unlocked. It swung slowly open when they touched it. Sally peered into the darkness.

"I can't see any bikes," she whispered, "I can't see anything."

"One of us will have to sneak in and look around," whispered John. "You stand guard. I'll be back in a minute."

"Hold on," protested Sally. "I want to do it."

"We can't both do it," argued John. "One of us has to keep watch to make sure the crooks don't sneak up from behind."

"But why can't *you* be the lookout?" demanded Sally.

"I'm the chief," explained John. "Besides, it's my bike."

John had a strong argument, but Sally made him flip a coin for it anyway, heads or tails. John won and disappeared silently into the basement. Sally kept watch on the steps outside, waiting impatiently for him to reappear. The minutes passed slowly, and finally Sally couldn't stand the suspense any longer.

"What are you doing in there?" she hissed into the

darkness. "I'm coming in to help, you're taking too long!"

"*Shhh*! Don't make a sound!" John whispered back. I've found the bikes. They're all stacked together, but I can't tell if one of them's mine. It's too dark and—wait a minute!"

There was a moment of silence followed by a loud crash. Sally gasped.

"John! What happened? Are you all right?" she called softly.

The basement lights snapped on. John was OK, but he lay trapped in the middle of a heap of fallen bicycles. Then Sally heard footsteps at the top of the inside stairs. She raced across the basement floor to pull John clear of the bicycles, but it was too late. Before Sally could rescue John, the two men had reached the bottom of the stairs.

"What's going on here?" The short man was standing over John, glowering down at him. John grinned up at the man triumphantly from the tangle of handlebars.

"I found it!" he cried. "I knew it was here!"

"Found what?" asked the man angrily.

"My bike. It's right here," said John, pointing.

The tall man cleared his throat, and the short man licked his lips nervously.

"You're making a big mistake, kid," said the tall man. "We bought these bikes second-hand from a friend of ours. That one may be the same colour as yours, but it's not your bike."

"Oh, yes it is!" declared John. "See the raccoon tail? I got that specially from the bike store just the other day."

The two men looked at each other for a long moment, and then the short man turned back to John.

"You and your friend stay still for a minute while I have a little talk with my partner."

Sally helped John to his feet as the two men huddled together. "We're in a real mess now," she whispered. "We have to do something."

"Looks like trouble all right," agreed John.

"I have a plan," Sally whispered. "You get them talking so that they won't notice me. I'll sneak over to the door. When I get a chance, I'll make a break for it and go for the police."

John nodded, but before he and Sally could discuss the plan, the two thieves had finished talking. The shorter man came over to John.

"Listen, kid," the man said with a crooked smile that looked fake around the edges. "You say that's your bike, so we believe you. My partner and I think our friend may be pulling a fast one with the second-hand bikes he's selling us. We've decided to report him to the police right away. In the meantime, why don't you just take your own bike and go home? If you and your friend get out of here fast, my partner and I won't even tell the police that you broke in illegally."

John thought it over quickly. He knew that the two men really had stolen the bikes themselves. But if he played along with them, they would let Sally and him go. It would be much safer than making a run for it, and he'd get his bike back for sure. Besides, nothing could stop him from going straight to the police and telling them where the thieves' hideout was. There was no time to talk it over with Sally—the crooks might change their minds.

"Sounds fair to me," John replied.

The short man grinned at his partner. "See, I told you the boy would want to get his bike back. Come on, let's help him on his way."

As the two crooks bent over the tangle of bikes, John looked over at Sally and winked. But Sally didn't wink back. She wasn't even looking at John. Slowly, silently she was edging closer to the outside door. Suddenly John realized that Sally hadn't been listening at all. She was still planning to make a run for it. That would ruin everything.

"Sally!" he called desperately, "Wait a minute!"

It was too late. Sally was already running out the door.

The short man spun around and shouted to his partner. "Bill! After her! Quick!"

Bill let the bicycle he was holding crash to the floor as he raced out the door.

John could hear a loud scuffle outside in the driveway. Sally shouted once, and then everything was still again. John groaned. The short man smiled with relief and started moving slowly towards John.

"Sounds as if your friend didn't get far," said the short man in a low, threatening voice. He stepped over the fallen bicycle directly in front of John, who was backing away cautiously.

"Hold it right there!" came a voice from the door.

John and the thief both froze, and then glanced over to see who had spoken. A police officer was crossing the doorway. A second followed close behind, along with the sad-looking thief, Bill. Then Sally and the cabdriver came running over to John. While the two police officers questioned the crooks, the cabdriver described his part in the adventure to John and Sally.

"When I drove back around the block, you were nowhere in sight," the cabdriver explained. "I thought you might be in trouble, so I called the police. There was a cruiser near by. The police arrived just in time to catch that big guy who was chasing Sally."

The cabdriver pointed at Bill, who slouched over and glumly shook his head. John shot a look towards the pile of bikes.

"We were right about those two being the thieves," he said.

"You certainly were," agreed the cabdriver. "They have plenty of bikes stashed down here. . . . Say, that one over by the wall looks just like my son's bike, the one that was stolen two weeks ago!"

John and Sally helped the cabdriver pull a green-and-gold bicycle free from the others. The police officers looked on with interest as the cabdriver checked it over. The short thief glared at John. The tall one kept his eyes on the floor.

Soon after, when reporters came to John's house, Sally and John proudly retold the story of how they had solved the case of the missing bike. The newspaper ran the whole story the next day.

"B.A.D. KIDS MAKE GOOD!" shouted the headline. There was even a picture of the detectives and the cabdriver who had helped them.

"The Barton Avenue Detectives are off and rolling," John declared excitedly at the next meeting of the club. "Nothing can stop us now! Everyone knows that the kids from B.A.D. always solve the crime. We're going to be famous, you wait and see."

"I can't wait to see what our next case will be!" added Sally as the other detectives nodded in enthusiastic agreement.☐

Getting The Picture

Interview with Author Allen Morgan

by Mimi Garry

INTERVIEWER: Allen, many of the boys and girls who have read your stories and books would like to know more about you. They might like to know if you enjoyed writing when you were in school.

ALLEN: Yes, I did enjoy it and I was fairly good at it. I liked thinking up story ideas. But I always had trouble sitting down and actually starting to write the story.

INTERVIEWER: I guess most children find that hard. Did it get easier as you grew up?

ALLEN: No, sitting down and getting started is still difficult for me. I probably spend half an hour every day getting ready to write. I usually do lots of little things around the house. Then I start writing. If you're going to be a professional writer, you have to write every day, whether you feel like it or not.

INTERVIEWER: Boys and girls often ask authors where their ideas come from. Where do yours come from?

ALLEN: A lot of thoughts seem to rush through my mind at times. I usually write them down when they come to me.

INTERVIEWER: Do your ideas come from experiences you're having?

ALLEN: Usually they start out as images, or pictures, in my mind.

INTERVIEWER: Could you give me an example?

ALLEN: Sure. I might see something interesting, like a barber pole. You don't see too many of them around any more. But there used to be a red-and-white-striped pole in front of every barbershop.

INTERVIEWER: What could you do with an image like that?

ALLEN: I might say to myself, "That's an interesting idea for a picture book. Not many people have written about barber poles. Why were they put outside barbershops? What did they tell people? How could I build a story around them?" Then I jot the words *barber pole* on a slip of paper and tack the slip to a bulletin board. Maybe I won't use that idea for a year or more, but it's tacked up where I can see it.

INTERVIEWER: Do you keep on making notes like that to yourself?

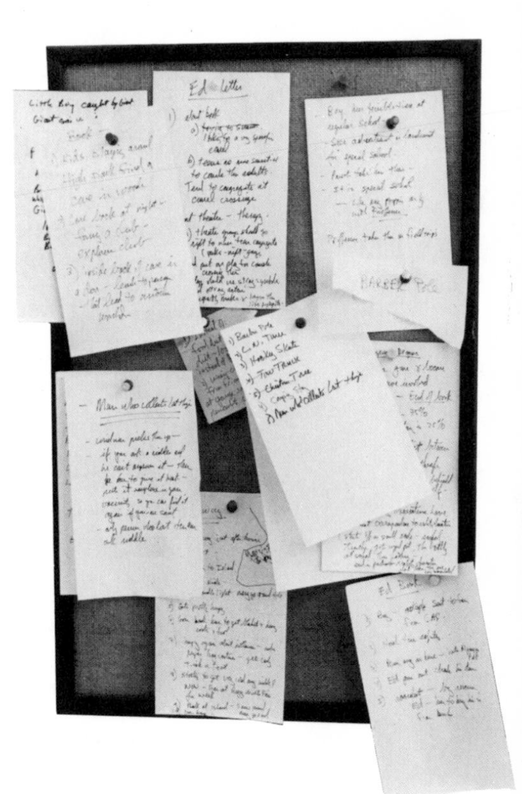

ALLEN: Oh, yes. I might think that barber poles and polar bears go together. So I jot that down. After a while, I go over all those little slips of paper to see which ideas look best. When I write a picture book, I usually start with six different ideas. Out of those six, four will seem pretty good. Then I cut the four to two. Finally I choose one to work on.

INTERVIEWER: Do you go through the same process when you're writing a longer book?

ALLEN: Yes. Sometimes I have six, seven, or eight pictures in my mind before I start writing. The pictures are like islands. I have to figure out how to get from one island to the next.

INTERVIEWER: These images seem really important to your writing.

ALLEN: They are. I think about an image and my feelings about it for two or three days. If there are people in my image, they start to do things. It's sort of like seeing a movie that's frozen or stopped on one frame. When I sit down and think about it, I get the movie going.

INTERVIEWER: Then what do you do?

ALLEN: First I usually write an outline of the story. I need to see where I'm going. I have to find paths from one idea, or one island, to another.

INTERVIEWER: Does that make the beginning of a story hard or easy?

ALLEN: For me, the beginning is easy. Starting things off is exciting because the story can go anywhere I want it to. And if the beginning doesn't work out, I can throw it away and start again. Sometimes I write a whole opening scene that I never use. But it's still fun. And I don't feel I've wasted time, because I always learn something from what I write.

INTERVIEWER: Is it the same experience every time—exploring ideas as you would explore islands and then linking them up?

ALLEN: It's different every time. Sometimes I get the ending of a story before I know how it begins. Other times, the ending comes on its own.

INTERVIEWER: Do the characters you write about help you to tell the story?

ALLEN: They definitely do. They seem to talk to each other in my head, and take me places I would never have thought of without them. But of course I have to choose what to write down.

INTERVIEWER: When you write about the Barton Avenue Detectives, do you let them talk to each other and do things that kids imagine and dream about?

ALLEN: I sure do. When I was a kid, I used to lie in bed at night and imagine myself solving crimes or being kidnapped. I'd play situations like that over and over in my mind just for fun.

INTERVIEWER: And now you let the B.A.D. kids have all sorts of fantastic adventures.

ALLEN: They do have daring adventures. Many of the things in a B.A.D. kids story might never actually happen. But they would all be possible in your imagination. I look for adventurous ideas that boys and girls would like to fantasize about.

INTERVIEWER: Is revising a story difficult?

ALLEN: Yes. Sometimes I edit things too soon, and that's a problem.

INTERVIEWER: Why is that a problem?

ALLEN: When you edit a story, you move pieces around and change them. And you cut some parts out. It's like making a sculpture. But you have to be careful. If you are sculpting rock and you cut away too much too soon, you lose the shape you're trying to get.

INTERVIEWER: Do you edit all your stories?

ALLEN: Yes. I always write too much. My stories are usually twice as long as they should be.

INTERVIEWER: You've been a teacher and a taxicab driver, as well as a writer. Did you enjoy these jobs?

ALLEN: I liked teaching. I especially liked teaching kindergarten. The children played out fantasies all the time. I like to do that, too. I've written a lot of stories for kindergarten kids. Now I'm making those stories into a TV series.

INTERVIEWER: And what about driving a taxicab?

ALLEN: The great thing about driving a taxicab is that you get to see a whole city in a way you never see it when you are doing other things. You can see what everybody's doing, and you get a feeling that the city is alive. You run into all kinds of wonderful events and feelings.

INTERVIEWER: You seem to enjoy the world very much.

ALLEN: I do. I enjoy being alive. One of the best ways for me to find out what I'm thinking and feeling is through writing. I think kids can do that, too.□

EYE
CATCHERS
EYECATCHERSEYECATCHERS
EYECATCHERSEYECATCHERSEYECATCHERS

THE TOP

I
AM A
TINY
SPINNING TOP
NOW IN A RHYME
HOW CAN I STOP
? ? ? ? ? ? ? ? ?
??????????
???
?

by Colleen Thibaudeau

FISH BARBEQUE

Light the light
fire the fire
now
fillet the fillets
dress the dressings
fix the fixings
then
spread the spread
dish the dishes
eat the eats
taste the taste
and
savour the savour
now
pop the pop
toast a toast
and
feast the feast

by Meguido Zola

If you stood with your feet in the earth
Up to your ankles in grass
And your arms had leaves running over them
And every once in a while one of your leafy fingers
Was nudged by a bird flying past,
If the skin that covers you from top to tip
Wasn't skin at all, but bark
And you never moved your feet from their place
In the earth
But stood rooted in that one spot come
Rain
Wind
Snow
Sleet
Thaw
Spring
Summer
Winter
Fall
Blight
Bug
Day
Dark
Then you would be me:
A tree.

by Karla Kuskin

s k y

rainrainrain
rainrainrainrainrainrain
rainrainrainrainrainr**CLOUD**inrain
rainrainr**CLOUD**inrainrainrainrain
rainrainrainr**CLOUD**inrainrain
rainrainrainrainrainrainrainrain
rainrainra**CLOUD**nrainrainrainrain
rainrainrainrain
rainrainrainrain
rain
rainrain
rain

a

r i

n

by Mary Ellen Solt

WORMS

Worms
are
very
long
and
thin
and
birds
just
love
to
eat
'em.
I'd
stick
to
beef
if
I
were
you
'cause
steers
have
got
more
meat
on.

by Jan Andrews

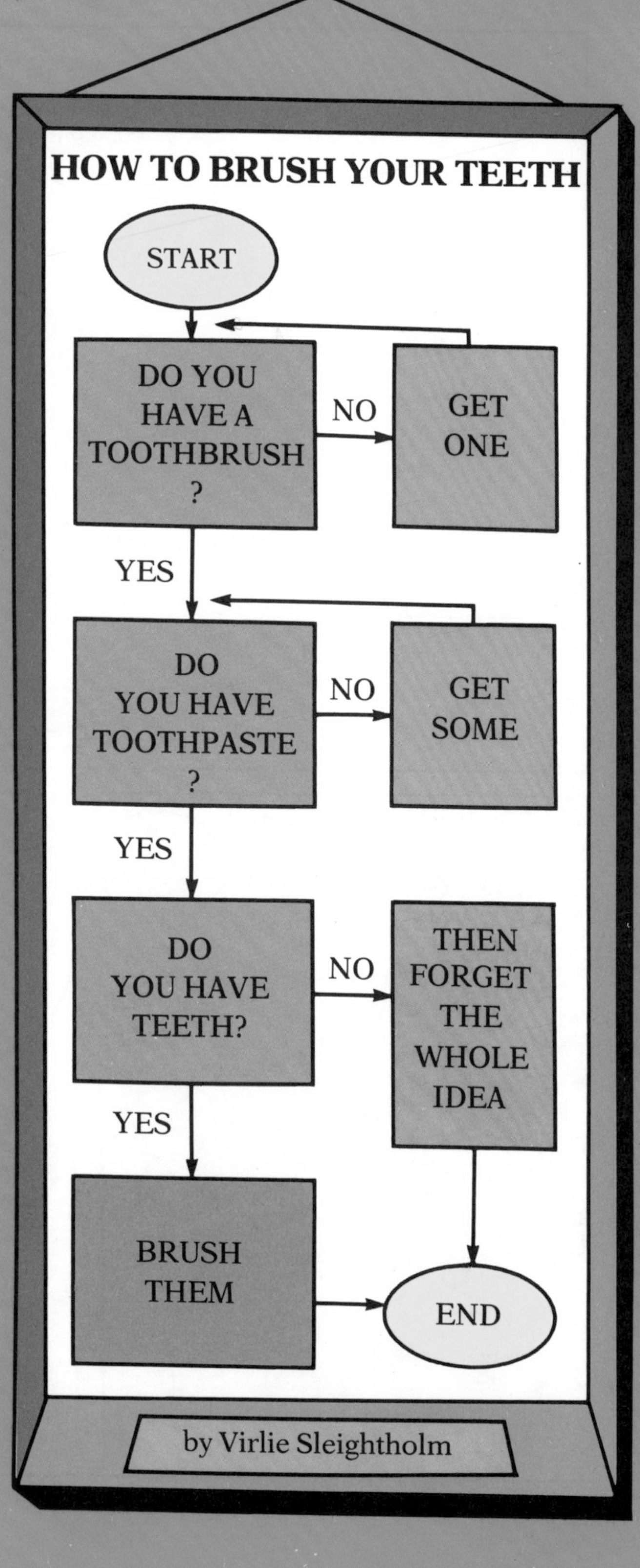

World Without M

by Dennis Pelrine

TOO LATE! YOU ARE BANISHED FRO* THE KINGDO* FOR SAYING THAT AWFUL NA*E. NO ONE *UST EVER SAY IT AGAIN.
BUT SON...
BUT KING MABEL...

IT'S YOUR FAULT. WHEN I WAS A BABY, YOU CALLED *E BY A GIRL'S NA*E. GET OUT! BE GONE!

EXIT

TODAY I A* YOUR NEW KING! KING *ABEL! FRO* NOW AND FOREVER THE USE OF THIS LETTER IS FORBIDDEN. IT WILL NEVER BE WRITTEN OR SPOKEN.
M

8
NEW LAWS OF THE LAND
① ANYONE CAUGHT USING THE FORBIDDEN LETTER WILL BE SENT TO THE SALT *INES.
② LAUGHING AND S*ILING ARE FORBIDDEN.
③ THE USE OF *ONEY IS FORBIDDEN.

9
HE HAS TO BE JOKING. YOU CAN'T JUST GET RID OF M.
YOU USED THE FORBIDDEN LETTER AND YOU LAUGHED. OFF TO THE *INES.
MARK
MANDY

10
THE NEW KING IS MAD. HOW CAN WE GET ALONG WITHOUT MONEY?
YOU ARE ARRESTED. YOU USED THE FORBIDDEN LETTER TWICE.

THE NEXT DAY...
THAT ROTTEN KING. HE HAS TO GO!
ALL BECAUSE OF THAT KING, WE HAVE TO CHANGE OUR NAMES.

*ARK! YOU *UST NEVER TALK LIKE THAT. YOU'LL BE SENT TO THE SALT *INES.

*ARK AND *ANDY'S
HIDEOUT

EVERYBODY HAS TO CALL *E *ARK AND YOU *ANDY JUST BECAUSE HE'S *AD. I WANT *Y NA*E BACK.
I DO TOO. BUT WHAT CAN WE DO?

15
YOU MUST BE CAREFUL, MARK. OOOOPS - I JUST USED THE TERRIBLE LETTER M. I HOPE THERE'S NO ONE AROUND.
WE'LL THINK OF A PLAN.

16
BACK IN THE SQUARE THE NEXT DAY...
I HEAR THAT SO*E OF YOU STIL HAVE *ONEY. I WANT IT ALL TURNED IN. I WANT YOUR CHILDREN TO BRING ALL THE *ONEY TO THE COUNTING HOUSE AT *Y PALACE.

17
IF THE ROO* IS NOT FILLED WITH *ONEY WHEN I OPEN THE DOOR, ALL THE CHILDREN WILL BE SENT TO THE *INES.

18
THAT DAY AT THE HIDEOUT...
IS EVERYONE SURE OF OUR PLAN?
YES!
GO!
ARK

19
GO HO*E AND TELL YOUR PARENTS ABOUT OUR PLAN. FRIDAY NIGHT WE DELIVER ALL THE *ONEY THE DU*B KING ASKED FOR. HE'LL GET STUCK WITH *ORE OF IT THAN HE CAN HANDLE.

20
COUNTING HOUSE
ALL RIGHT, GANG. LET'S FILL THE KING'S ROO* WITH *ONEY.

21
WE WORKED ALL NIGHT. WE'RE FINISHED.
HERE CO*ES THE KING.

22
WHAT A BEAUTIFUL DAY! SOON I'LL BE ROLLING IN ALL THAT BEAUTIFUL *ONEY.

23
AAACCHGH!
HORRAAHHH!
HA! HA!
HA!

24
TO THE CITY GATES

25
GOOD BYE, MABEL!
DON'T COME BACK!
ENJOY YOUR *ONEY!
TO THE *INES

26
WELCOME HOME
FORMER KING AND QUEEN
THANK YOU, EVERYONE. NOW WE WILL HAVE OUR FEAST.
MARK
MANDY
OF MUFFINS
MELONS
MACAROONS
MANGOES
MACARONI
MARSHMALLOWS
MUSHROOMS
MARMALADE

27
I'LL SEND THIS MILKSHAKE AND THESE M AND M's TO OUR DEAR SON MABEL. HE MUST BE TIRED OF *ONEY BY NOW.
GOOD IDEA, DEAR. MMMMMM.
M-M

The Special Moment

by John McInnes

The special moment happens . . .
  when we understand each other.
The special moment happens . . .
  when we know that others care.
The special moment happens . . .
  when our friends are there
    to share
The special moment.

GETTING TOGETHER

The Dip

by Jan Andrews

The dip was Tick Merrick's place. It was down by the abandoned beaver lodge where the stream flowed and the bare elms rose out of ferns and brush. Tick hugged the possession of it fiercely to himself, and went there often. He was glad that at last he had found a place where he did not have to screw up his small, sharp face and act tough.

But then the other kid came, and everything changed. As soon as Tick saw her, his heart sank. She was walking slowly, just as he had walked when he came to the dip for the first time. He knew that she too was looking for a place of her own.

Holding his breath, Tick ducked behind a stand of raspberry canes. Maybe if he kept still and out of sight, she would wander away and never come back. Tick bit his lip as a chipmunk squeaked at the girl. She grinned, pushed her black, shaggy hair from her eyes, and settled herself comfortably against a tree trunk. Tick knew then that there was no hope. The girl wouldn't go away. Springing up, he ran over to stand on the bank at the edge of the stream.

"What are you doing here? Who are you, anyhow?" he hollered.

The girl looked up, startled. "I'm Peggy," she shouted back.

"You get out," he yelled across the water at her. "You just get on out of here!"

The other kid was on her feet again in an instant. "Why?" she challenged.

"'Cause—Because it's mine here."

"Who says?"

"I do!"

Tick jumped into the stream and waded across, his small, brown eyes glowering, and his fists tight and ready. He wanted the girl to run, but she would not.

Instead, she planted her feet solidly on the bank and waited for him.

"You can't be here! You can't!" Tick spat out at her.

"I can so! I can!" Peggy shot back.

The dip was spoiled for Tick after that. Every day when he went there, he and Peggy fought. They argued, called names, and threatened each other. At last, Tick declared a truce.

"OK," he called out in exasperation. "OK. You can have one side of the stream. It's—it's yours. But the right side's mine, and you keep off it. Don't you touch it, not even with a finger! You hear?" Tick received a sneering nod of reply.

Peggy kept to the agreement, but still Tick was not happy. Now he came to the dip not to enjoy it, but to guard and watch. There was no peace in it for him any more.

Through the long summer, things went on like that. Then, one late August morning as Tick and Peggy each prowled their own sides of the stream, Tick scared a duck out of a clump of reeds. The duck hurled itself forward, limping headlong into the water. Then it flapped its wings frantically. It was trying to lift itself into the air.

"It's hurt," Peggy shouted to Tick from the other side of the stream. "It can't fly."

Peggy glanced at Tick. But before Tick could say anything, she was wading out after the fluttering bird. He was about to call out to warn her that she was crossing the invisible border line down the stream's middle. But the duck flapped still more desperately. Tick started running.

"I'll head it off!" he cried.

"Hurry," Peggy yelled back. "I've almost got it."

The duck saw Tick and hesitated. In an instant Peggy

surged forward and gathered the blur of brown-and-white feathers in her grasp. The bird writhed and twisted, almost escaping. Without thinking, Tick tore off his jacket.

"Here!" he cried as he too waded into the stream. "Give it to me. I'll wrap it in this."

Peggy handed the duck over to Tick, and a look passed between them.

"We'll—we'll take it to my side," he said.

Shivering from the cold water, they climbed the bank onto dry land. As Tick gently unwrapped his burden, Peggy's grimy hands reached towards it.

"I said it was hurt, didn't I?" she burst out.

One of the duck's wings hung limp and twisted. As Tick and Peggy looked closer, they saw that one of its legs was also bent.

"Think we could fix it?" Tick asked, narrowing his brown eyes.

"We could try," the girl said with fierce determination.

Again the look passed between them.

"We both found it, didn't we?" Tick said.

Peggy flicked at her shaggy cowlick. "Yes," she agreed.

From then on there wasn't much time for feuding. The duck took all Tick's and Peggy's attention. They bandaged its wing and made a splint for its leg. They kept it in a box and took turns having it at home at night. Together they even made a raft for the duck so that it could sit out in the stream for a few minutes, floating on the water.

Tick and Peggy watched and tenderly cared for the duck. But despite their efforts, it did not do well. Mainly, it would not eat. The carefully gathered worms and scraps of lettuce...the bits of hamburger...the waterweed...all were ignored.

"It wants to die, doesn't it," Peggy said one morning as the duck huddled miserably in its box.

"I think so," Tick answered bleakly.

"I think so, too."

Peggy seemed about to say something else but changed her mind. Tick cleared his throat. He had been about to say something as well. He changed his mind, too.

The duck lived the rest of that day and into the next. Then, suddenly and quietly, it died. Tick and Peggy took the light, cold body and laid it on the raft they had made. They decorated the raft with leaves and sent it floating away. As it neared a bend in the stream, Peggy's eyes filled with tears.

"I'll go now," she said unsteadily.

Tick swallowed. "You don't have to," he answered, hunching his shoulders and jamming his hands into his pockets.

"You were here first," Peggy reminded him.

"I gave you a side of the stream, didn't I?"

"Only because I wouldn't leave."

The girl began to trudge away through dead leaves and grass.

"I *said* you could stay," Tick called after her.

Peggy turned to face him, standing small and tense and firm. "I don't want to stay if you mind," she said clearly.

"Yeah, well, I don't. I don't mind, not any more."

"Really?"

"Really."

"OK then." Peggy headed back across the stream, climbed the bank, and sat down.

The dip was Tick Merrick's place once again. His and Peggy's. They went there often.□

The Christmas Easter Egg

by Zonia Keywan

Long ago when pioneers from Europe were first settling in the West, a little Ukrainian girl named Hanusia lived on a homestead with her parents and her two small brothers. The family lived in a tiny wooden house at the edge of their farm, and they were very poor.

Every day, Hanusia went to a one-room schoolhouse along with other children of all ages. A few of the students were from families who had lived in Canada for many years. But most of them had only recently arrived. There were Ukrainian children, like Hanusia. There were also children who had come from Poland, Germany, Sweden, and other countries.

One winter day Hanusia saw a group of girls standing together in the schoolyard. They were whispering and laughing. They seemed very excited.

Hanusia tried to slip past the girls, because one of them was Marta Nilsson. Marta was a year younger than Hanusia, but she was big and loud and bossy. Hanusia did not like Marta because the Nilsson girl often laughed at her for not knowing how to speak English well.

"Hanusia!" Marta cried out. "We were talking about the presents we're going to give the teacher at the Christmas party. What are you going to bring?"

Hanusia's hand leaped to her mouth.

"What's the matter?" Marta asked with a mean little smile. "Don't you know that we're giving presents to Miss Grady?"

"I know," Hanusia answered. "I...I did not decide yet."

But the truth was that Hanusia did not know at all. How could she know? This was her first Christmas in a Canadian school.

Marta puffed herself out to look bigger than ever. "I'm going to give Miss Grady the biggest bottle of perfume in my father's store," she announced boastfully. Marta's father owned the only store in the town near by. When Hanusia went to town with her parents, she liked to look at all the lovely things Mr. Nilsson sold in his store.

"We have some little plants in the parlour at home," Laura Brown chimed in. "I'm going to bring one for Miss Grady." Laura always tagged along behind Marta and imitated everything she did.

"I'm going to get my mother to knit her some warm mittens," said Erica Schultz. Erica was a small, blonde German girl. Her family, like Hanusia's, had recently come to Canada.

What will I do? Hanusia wondered all the way home. The Christmas party was only a week away, but now she wished it would never come. How could she get Miss Grady a present in such a short time? She had no money at all, and her parents certainly had no money to give her. Hanusia's mother was always worrying about how little they had. Every penny her father earned went for important things such as food for the family and tools for the farm.

That evening Hanusia could not keep her mind on her chores. First she forgot to fetch the pail of water her mother asked for. Then she had to be reminded three times to put more wood on the fire in the stove. Finally Hanusia took so long to peel the potatoes that her mother had to finish the job herself.

"What *is* the matter with you this evening?" her mother asked, shaking her head.

Hanusia took a deep breath. "Everybody at school is bringing Miss Grady a Christmas present," she said quickly. "Can I bring one, too?"

"You know that we can't afford to buy presents," her mother replied.

"But *everybody* is doing it," Hanusia protested. This was not quite true. She had heard only a few girls talking about presents, but she wanted to sound more convincing.

"Anyway, for us it isn't Christmas yet," her mother said. "We don't celebrate Christmas until January. And we don't give presents, except to children. Besides, Miss Grady won't expect all the children to bring presents. She knows that some are too poor. Don't worry, little one. Your teacher is kind. She will understand."

But Hanusia *did* worry. In fact, for the next few days she could think of nothing else. She tried hard to find something to give Miss Grady. She looked on every shelf in the little house. She checked under the beds and in every nook and cranny. She even searched all through the barn. But it was no use. She found nothing.

Then on the night before the party, Hanusia's mother said, "I've been thinking about your present for the teacher. I've had an idea."

Hanusia waited impatiently while her mother took a key from a nail on the wall and opened a large wooden trunk. The family had brought all their belongings to Canada in this trunk. Hanusia's mother pulled out a bundle and unwrapped the cloth that covered it. Inside was a dish of brightly coloured Easter eggs.

"Look!" said her mother. "You can pick out whichever egg you like best to give to Miss Grady."

Of all the Ukrainian women in the district, Hanusia's mother made the most beautiful *pysanky*, or Easter eggs. Her eggs had more intricate designs, straighter lines, and livelier colours than anyone else's. On Easter Sunday—when people from all around brought their eggs in baskets to be blessed in church—Hanusia always felt proud that her mother's eggs were the prettiest of all. But tonight the eggs did not make her happy.

"I can't give Miss Grady an Easter egg," she protested. "She would laugh at me if I gave her an Easter egg for Christmas."

"Well, it's all we have," her mother said. "If you change your mind, let me know."

And she put the eggs back in the trunk.

All that night Hanusia thought about Marta's perfume and Erica's mittens. Early the next morning she made up her mind. She would give Miss Grady one of her mother's Easter eggs.

Hanusia's mother opened the family trunk again. Slowly and carefully Hanusia examined each *pysanka*. She picked up one, then another, and then a third. At last she chose one. The egg was as colourful as a rainbow and covered all over with delicate lines and crosses. In the very centre was a pair of reindeer. Hanusia hoped that the reindeer would make the egg look more like Christmas.

In the schoolhouse the children chattered in excitement. Like Hanusia, many of them had never attended a Christmas party at school before. Hanusia gazed around the classroom in wonder. It was completely transformed. Red and green decorations hung everywhere, and the walls were covered with Christmas cards.

Miss Grady read the children the story of the first Christmas. The whole class sang carols. Then the teacher gave each child a parcel filled with cookies and candy of all kinds.

"Will you open your presents now, Miss Grady?" Marta asked in her sweetest voice.

One by one Miss Grady opened the presents that were piled on her desk. Hanusia recognized Marta's gift. It was a bottle of perfume, but it was not big at all. In fact, it was the smallest bottle Hanusia had ever seen.

Hanusia's present was the very last. Miss Grady undid the layers of cloth wrapping and held up the egg in her hand.

"But what is it, Hanusia?" she asked.

Miss Grady was new in the district and had never seen a Ukrainian Easter egg.

Ivan Shewchuk, one of the older Ukrainian boys, called out from the back of the room, "It's an *Easter egg*!" And he snickered loudly.

"An *Easter egg* for Christmas!" Marta exclaimed. She rolled her eyes and began to giggle. In no time at all the whole roomful of children was laughing.

"My mother made it," Hanusia said in a tiny voice. Her face was burning. I should never have brought that silly egg, she thought.

"Oh, Hanusia, what a beautiful gift!" said Miss Grady. "And how wonderful to get an Easter egg at Christmas! It makes me feel as if spring were here already."

One by one the children stopped laughing. Before long they had all crowded around Miss Grady's desk to look at her presents, especially the one from Hanusia.

Long after Christmas was past, the Easter egg sat perched in a little glass on Miss Grady's desk. Sometimes when Hanusia looked up from her work, she would see its bright colours shimmering in the sunlight. And then Hanusia would feel a little glow of pride and special happiness.□

Katie's Promise

by Bernice Thurman Hunter

Katie and Deena were best friends. They lived next door to each other and did everything together. They even looked alike. Both girls had long black hair, wide brown eyes, and spaces between their two front teeth. Katie and Deena were often mistaken for sisters. But they got along much better than most sisters do.

One day the girls had a fight. Oh, they'd had quarrels before—little squabbles and misunderstandings. But this was different. This was a real, bang-up, honest-to-goodness fight. It happened Friday afternoon on the way home from school.

"I hate you, Deena!" Katie hissed through her separated teeth. "And I'm never going to speak to you again as long as I live!"

"Well, you won't get the chance," Deena said scornfully, "because I'm not going to speak to you first . . . so there!" Flinging her long black mane over her shoulder, Deena turned on her heel and strode up her own front walk.

Seething with anger, Katie ran home. Once inside her house, she slammed the door, dropped her books, kicked off her boots, and headed straight for the kitchen. There she made herself a cup of hot soup and a chocolate ice-cream cone. Flopping down at the kitchen table, she ate them both at once.

A few moments later Katie heard her mother come in. A tripping, scrambling noise came from the hallway.

"Katrina!"

Katie jumped up, spilling the last of her soup.

"What?" she shouted crossly at her mother.

"Come here this minute and clean up this mess! I nearly broke my neck, tripping over your books and your boots."

Katie did as she was told.

During dinner Katie's mother talked pleasantly enough. But Katie just sulked and sighed and picked at her food.

Finally her mother asked, "What's the matter, dear?"

"I'm in a bad mood," said Katie.

"Well, I can see that . . . but why?"

"Oh, no reason." Katie quickly excused herself and left the table.

The next afternoon Katie just slouched on the chesterfield, watching her mother do the Saturday jobs that Katie was supposed to do. Out of the blue, her mother asked, "Where's Deena?"

"I don't know and I don't care!" snapped Katie.

"Well, you don't have to bite my head off!"

"I'm sorry, Mom," mumbled Katie, getting up and drifting out of the room.

Meanwhile, next door, Deena hunched on the window seat, staring moodily outside and munching on a potato-chip-and-pickle sandwich.

"You left half your lunch on your plate, and now you're stuffing yourself with junk," grumbled her father.

When Deena didn't answer, her father tried a different approach.

"Where's that shadow of yours?" he asked. "Did Katie take off for another planet?"

"I hope so!" growled Deena. Then she stomped out of the room and up the stairs.

And that's the way it was in both houses for the entire weekend.

On Monday morning Deena left for school early, and Katie left late. The minute Katie arrived in her classroom she marched straight up to the teacher's desk and asked Ms. Lewis to change her seat.

"What's wrong with the seat you have?" Ms. Lewis wanted to know.

"I can't see the chalkboard," lied Katie, crossing her fingers.

"When was your last eye examination?" Ms. Lewis sounded suspicious.

"Two weeks ago," admitted Katie.

"Then stop your nonsense, Katie. Sit down and get to work."

Katie dropped like a sack of potatoes into the seat behind Deena and glared at the back of her former friend's bent head.

The rest of the class had been listening attentively to Katie and Ms. Lewis. There was nothing they liked better to liven up a Monday morning than a bit of trouble—especially somebody else's trouble.

At recess Katie and Deena were each surrounded by a ring of nosy, animated classmates.

"Did you two have a fight?"

"Who started it?"

"What's it about?"

"I never liked Katie that much anyway."

"That Deena thinks she's so smart!"

Neither girl said a thing. Except for Carol, the others soon lost interest. When the noon bell rang, Carol sidled up to Katie and whispered, "Can *I* be your best friend now, Katie?"

Katie knew that Deena didn't like Carol. Making friends with Carol might be a good way to get back at Deena.

Katie shrugged her shoulders. "I guess so," she said carelessly.

After school Marty ran to catch up with Deena. Marty had had a crush on Deena since the beginning of the year, but he had always been a little afraid of Katie.

"Can I walk home with you today, Deena?" he asked hopefully.

"I don't care," answered Deena coolly.

By the end of that week everybody seemed to have forgotten that Katie and Deena had once been best friends. Everybody, that is, except Katie and Deena.

At home Katie moped around or lay listlessly in front of the television, pretending to do her homework. She wasn't a moper by nature. And she wasn't a TV addict either, so her mother began to worry.

"Why don't you make up with Deena?" she asked tactfully.

"I'd rather die!" barked Katie.

Katie's mother winced and bit her lip to keep from barking back.

"I'm sorry, Mom," Katie apologized.

Next door, things weren't going any better.

"You used to pick up after yourself and help around here," observed Deena's father, stuffing newspapers and candy wrappers and assorted junk into a green garbage bag. "Now all you ever do is make a mess and talk on the phone to Marty with your feet up on the wall. Just look at that wall! All heel marks. And the telephone's on the floor again. For two cents I'd have the crummy thing disconnected."

Deena sighed, rose from her chair, and plunked down the phone on its table with such a bang that the "crummy thing" jangled in protest.

"If you ask me . . ." Her father gave the garbage bag a furious twirl and fastened it with a twist-tie. "If you ask me, Deena, this change in you has come about since you stopped being friends with Katie." He shot a look in her direction, and their eyes met unexpectedly. Deena's were swimming with tears. "Why don't you give Katie a call?" Deena's father suggested gently.

"No way!" Deena rubbed her eyes defiantly and stomped up to her room, slamming the door behind her.

Suddenly her father's patience turned to anger. Lunging over to the stairs, he yelled up after her, "Being a single parent is no picnic, you know!"

"Being an only child isn't either!" Deena yelled back.

That night Deena heard her father talking to her aunt on the phone. He was describing Deena's behaviour, and he sounded very worried. Deena felt ashamed. Before she went to bed, she told her father she was sorry she had worried him.

The weeks seemed to drag by for the two girls, who continued to avoid each other. Katie would peer through the curtains to make sure the coast was clear before heading out the door. And Deena would walk blocks out of her way so that she wouldn't run into Katie.

By now nobody else was paying much attention.

"I guess it's natural to outgrow old friends and make new ones," Deena's father observed. "Variety is the spice of life."

But Deena wasn't so sure. Soon she couldn't stand Marty any more. All he ever talked about was hockey, hockey, hockey!

And Katie wasn't happy either. She missed having a best friend who could keep a secret. Katie had quickly found out that she couldn't share more than a bag of jelly beans with Carol—the big blabbermouth!

But they were so much alike, Katie and Deena. Both were so stubborn and proud and foolish that neither would dream of giving in.

Then one day Katie stayed after school to help Ms. Lewis set up the science project for the next day. Science was Katie's favourite subject, and she enjoyed discussing it with her teacher. Ms. Lewis was smart—and friendly too—once you got to know her. Besides, staying after school gave Katie a perfect excuse not to walk home with Carol.

Before Katie knew it, an hour had gone by. "I should phone my mom," she said, glancing up at the big clock above the chalkboard. "She's a real worrywart."

"You can use the phone in the teachers' lounge," suggested Ms. Lewis. "I'll finish up here."

Katie's footsteps echoed eerily down the long corridor. The familiar halls seemed spooky when they were deserted. Hesitantly she opened the door to the teachers' lounge. She felt sort of guilty because the room was usually off limits to students. But Ms. Lewis had given her permission, after all. She would make her call and leave again as quickly as possible.

A black phone hung on the far wall. Katie's heels sounded like hammer blows as she crossed the wooden floor. She picked up the receiver and dialled the number. It rang once, twice, three times. She glanced nervously over her shoulder—she hoped her mother was home. Katie was about to hang up on the eighth ring when she heard the receiver click at the other end.

"Hello?"

The hair on Katie's neck sprang up. "Hello...? Who's that?"

There was a long pause, and then a puzzled voice said, "Is that you, Katie?"

There was another long pause. Then Katie answered, "Yes. . . . Is that you, Deena?"

"Yes, it's Deena, but . . . what's the matter, Katie? Are you all right? Do you need me? Why did you phone me, Katie?"

"I—I—I. . . . Oh, Deena, I just wanted to say I'm sorry!"

"Oh, Katie! I'm sorry, too. It was all my fault."

"No, it was my fault, Deena. But let's not fight about it. Let's just be friends again. OK?"

"OK!" Deena agreed in a joyful shout. "Dad! Dad!" Katie heard Deena calling. "It's Katie! We're friends again."

"By the way, Deena. . . ." Katie hesitated before she asked the question. "What did we fight about? I can't remember."

There was another long pause at the other end of the phone line. "I don't know—I can't remember either. . . . Isn't that silly? But who cares? Will you come over to my house, Katie, right now?"

"I'm on my way," laughed Katie, banging down the receiver. Then she remembered to phone her mother. "Mom, I'll be late getting home. I stayed to help Ms. Lewis, and now I'm going over to Deena's. That's right, Mom. Deena's. . . . We've made up."

Hurrying home in the twilight, Katie decided to make a promise to herself. It would be a secret and solemn vow. And for this she needed something important to swear on. She could cross her heart, of course, but that didn't seem right for this occasion. Then she noticed the first star of the evening in the darkening sky. It hung there against the blue velvet backdrop—a single silver star.

"I swear by the silver star," Katie said in a hushed voice. "I swear that I'll never tell anyone, as long as I live, that I dialled Deena's number by mistake!"□

Baby Talk

a play in two acts

by Wayne Carley

The Characters
(in order of appearance)

ROBERTS, a research assistant
BABY, a chimpanzee
PROFESSOR LINDERS, head of the project
MIDGE, the switchboard operator
DOCTOR KING, head of the university

plus

REPORTERS
PHOTOGRAPHERS
TELEVISION JOURNALISTS
TELEVISION CAMERA OPERATORS

ACT ONE

The Setting:
A research laboratory in the University of Scientific Studies. It is a white room full of machinery—computer terminals, tape recorders, typewriters, calculators, and so on. At the back of the lab is a large cage. In it, asleep on a pile of cushions, is BABY, a young chimpanzee.

Research assistant ROBERTS is at his desk with his feet propped up. He also is fast asleep.

The Time:
Monday, 8:30 a.m.

AS THE CURTAIN RISES:
(*PROFESSOR LINDERS enters. She sees ROBERTS and is annoyed that he is asleep. She leans over him and shouts in his ear.*)

PROFESSOR LINDERS: Roberts, wake up!
ROBERTS (*waking with a start*): What? What is it? (*He sees PROFESSOR LINDERS.*) Oh, oh.
PROFESSOR LINDERS: You were asleep.
ROBERTS: No, I wasn't, Professor Linders—honest. I was just resting my eyes.
PROFESSOR LINDERS: That's the third time this week I've found you sleeping on the job.
ROBERTS: You've got to believe me. I wasn't sleeping. I was... I was thinking!
PROFESSOR LINDERS: You were snoring.
ROBERTS: No, I wasn't. That's just a sound I make when I'm thinking. Listen. (*He assumes a pose of deep thought and makes a loud snoring sound.*) Some people think it's cute.
PROFESSOR LINDERS: Well, I'm not one of them. I've told you time and time again that you must stay alert. What if Baby had said her first word, and you weren't awake to hear it? Years of work would have been wasted.
ROBERTS (*hanging his head*): I know. I'm sorry. Please, Professor Linders, give me another chance. I really need this job.
PROFESSOR LINDERS: Well...
ROBERTS: Please?
PROFESSOR LINDERS: All right. But no more sleeping on night duty. Is that clear?
ROBERTS: Yes, Ma'am.
PROFESSOR LINDERS: Now tell me how Baby was last night.

ROBERTS: Well, she was a bit restless and wouldn't go to sleep. So I read her a story and she settled down.

PROFESSOR LINDERS: What story?

ROBERTS: Cinderella—what else? If I try to read her anything else, she screams her head off.

PROFESSOR LINDERS (*smiling fondly at the sleeping chimpanzee*): Yes, she is fond of Cinderella.

ROBERTS: Professor Linders, can I ask you a question? Do you really think that chimp is going to talk?

PROFESSOR LINDERS (*shocked*): Of course she'll talk. I've been exposing her to human language since she was one day old.

ROBERTS: But she's four years old now and all she does is grunt.

PROFESSOR LINDERS: Those grunts are the beginnings of words. One day soon Baby will go beyond grunts—she will speak to express the poetry in her soul.

ROBERTS: Well, I'm sorry, but sometimes I suspect that Baby is making a real monkey out of us all. (*MIDGE enters carrying coffee in a cardboard cup.*)

MIDGE: Good morning, you two. I thought I'd come in and have a coffee before I open the switchboard. Well, and did we all have a nice weekend?

PROFESSOR LINDERS: I did, thank you. Roberts doesn't know if he did or not. He slept through it.

ROBERTS: Aw, come on, Professor Linders.

MIDGE (*going to BABY'S cage and knocking on the bars*): And what about Baby? Did ooo-ums have a nice weekend, sweety-didums? (*The chimpanzee wakes up and begins to chatter in chimp talk.*)

PROFESSOR LINDERS: Midge, I've asked you before to please not use baby talk when you address Baby.

MIDGE: Why? She likes it, don't you, sweetums? (*She picks up a banana*.) Does the pwetty baby want her bwekkies? Nice yum-yum nana for bwekkies? (*BABY screams and reaches through the bars for the banana. At that moment DOCTOR KING enters carrying a handful of bills*.)

DOCTOR KING: What's going on here? Why aren't you all at work? (*to MIDGE*) Why isn't the switchboard open yet?

MIDGE: Because I'm on my coffee break. Besides, nobody ever calls until ten. And don't shout. It upsets Baby.

DOCTOR KING: That's another thing! Linders, do you know what these are? Bills! And do you know what they're for? Bananas! That chimp is eating us all out of our jobs. I'm afraid we can't afford to continue. You'll have to sell her to a zoo.

PROFESSOR LINDERS: Oh, no, Doctor King! We can't stop now. She's just about ready to talk. I know she is. I can feel it!

DOCTOR KING: How can she talk? Her mouth is always full of expensive bananas! No, I'm afraid I'll have to cancel the project and you'll have to get rid of her. (*Throughout this, BABY has settled down and is listening. Then she moves slowly to the bars, reaches through, and takes DOCTOR KING'S hand*.)

BABY: Dada.

PROFESSOR LINDERS (*in amazement*): Doctor King!

DOCTOR KING: No, don't try to talk me out of it—my mind is made up. We've got to get on with more meaningful work.

MIDGE (*whispering to ROBERTS*): Did you hear it?

ROBERTS: Yes, I heard it. But I still don't believe it.

DOCTOR KING: Why are you all staring at me?

MIDGE: She talked.

DOCTOR KING: What?

ROBERTS: Baby talked.

DOCTOR KING: No, she didn't. I didn't hear anything. You're all just trying to protect your jobs.

PROFESSOR LINDERS: No, she talked. Let's be quiet—maybe she'll say something else. (*They all fall silent and stare at BABY. BABY, turning coy, hides her face with her hands. Then she peeks through her fingers at DOCTOR KING.*)

BABY: Dada.

DOCTOR KING: Oh, my!

PROFESSOR LINDERS: She talked! She talked!

MIDGE: She sounded real cute, too.

BABY (*getting carried away*): Dada. Dada. Dada.

DOCTOR KING (*in a daze*): Do you know what this means? This chimp will put our university on the map forever. We'll be famous. We'll be rich! There'll be no limit to the number of experiments we'll be able to do. I've got to get on the phone and start telling people.

MIDGE: You can't. The switchboard isn't open yet.

DOCTOR KING (*shouting*): Well, open it!

MIDGE (*putting down her coffee*): All right, all right. (*to PROFESSOR LINDERS*) Listen, if you have any time today, would you see if you could teach her my name? I think it'd be real cute. (*She exits.*)

DOCTOR KING: Let's see—whom will I call first? The president of the university, of course. And maybe the provincial Premier and the Prime Minister—why not?

ROBERTS: Don't forget the press. I think you should call a press conference.

DOCTOR KING: A press conference—of course! (*He slaps ROBERTS on the back.*) What was your name again, son?

ROBERTS: Roberts. I'm a research assistant.

DOCTOR KING: Well, Roberts, you're a wide-awake lad. (*ROBERTS gives PROFESSOR LINDERS a meaningful look*.) I want you to help me set up the conference—I want you to call every newspaper and TV station in the city.

PROFESSOR LINDERS: Please, Doctor King, don't you think it's too soon for so much publicity?

DOCTOR KING: Certainly not. This is the biggest research breakthrough of the century. Come on, Roberts. We've got a lot of phoning to do.

ROBERTS: Yes, sir! (*DOCTOR KING and ROBERTS exit*.)

PROFESSOR LINDERS (*begins to walk around the lab, wringing her hands and talking to herself*): Oh dear, what's going to happen now? It's too soon—I just know it's too soon.

BABY: Excuse me, Professor Linders...

PROFESSOR LINDERS (*shocked ... looking around to see who spoke*): What? Who said that?

BABY: I did. I'm sorry to bother you while you're so deep in thought, but I thought we should have a little chat before the press conference. There are a few... conditions, shall we say?... that I'd like to get cleared up first.

PROFESSOR LINDERS (*faltering*): But—but... ohhh. (*PROFESSOR LINDERS faints*.)

(*CURTAIN*)

ACT TWO

The Scene:
The same.

The Time:
A few minutes later.

AS THE CURTAIN RISES:
(PROFESSOR LINDERS is lying on the floor. BABY is working at the lock on her cage, trying to get out. PROFESSOR LINDERS comes to, looks around, and shakes her head.)

PROFESSOR LINDERS: What happened? Where am I?
BABY: You fainted. But I don't think you hurt yourself when you fell.
PROFESSOR LINDERS (*jumping to her feet*): Now I remember! You can talk! And not just baby talk—you can really talk.
BABY: Yes, I can really talk.
PROFESSOR LINDERS: It's a miracle. I have done what no scientist before me ever did.
BABY: Well, don't forget you had a little help.
PROFESSOR LINDERS: What do you mean? I had no help—I did it alone.
BABY: You had me.
PROFESSOR LINDERS: You? You're just a chimpanzee—what do you know? I was the one who taught you.
BABY: Yes, but I was the one who learned. (*She fiddles with the lock again*.)
PROFESSOR LINDERS: What are you doing?
BABY: I'm trying to get out of this dreary cage. I want to have a talk with you and I'd rather not speak through bars.

PROFESSOR LINDERS: What do you want to talk about?
BABY: I have a few conditions.
PROFESSOR LINDERS: What kind of conditions?
BABY: Let me out and I'll tell you.
PROFESSOR LINDERS: Do you promise to behave?
BABY: Oh, really! I wish you'd stop treating me like a child. Let me out or I'll never say another word.
PROFESSOR LINDERS: That's blackmail.
BABY: You bet it is. (*PROFESSOR LINDERS opens the cage and BABY steps out*.) Ah, that's better. I want a banana.
PROFESSOR LINDERS: No, you've had enough.
BABY (*screaming and jumping up and down*): I want a banana! Give me a banana or I won't talk!
PROFESSOR LINDERS: All right, all right! (*She hands BABY a banana*.) Now, let's get down to business.
BABY: OK, here are my conditions: I want a new cage—bigger—and decorated with pillows and slipcovers. A nice cheerful colour—I can never understand why you scientists don't like bright colours. Yellow would be nice, I think.
PROFESSOR LINDERS: Banana yellow, I suppose.
BABY: Exactly! And I want my own telephone, my own television, a video recorder, and every video game on the market.
PROFESSOR LINDERS: Anything else?
BABY: Yes, I'd like a word processor near my bedside table.
PROFESSOR LINDERS: You're quite clever, aren't you?

BABY: Did you think humans were the only clever species? (*PROFESSOR LINDERS turns away*.) Look, Linders, if you and I are to make this thing really pay off, we'll have to be partners.

PROFESSOR LINDERS: What do I get?

BABY: Why, you can have anything you want!

PROFESSOR LINDERS: All I ever wanted was for this experiment to work. And now it has. There doesn't seem to be any reason to go on.

BABY: Oh, come on, Professor, get hold of yourself. You're a scientist. There must be other experiments you'd like to try. How about teaching lab rats to tap-dance?

PROFESSOR LINDERS: What good are dancing rats?

BABY: What good is a talking chimp? But it does help pay the bills.

PROFESSOR LINDERS: I suppose so. And I *have* been curious about the hooting habits of the great horned owl.

BABY: There, you see? Already you're going on to bigger and better things. So, we're agreed?

PROFESSOR LINDERS: Yes, I guess so.

BABY: OK now, there's just one thing more. I don't think it would be smart to show them how well I really talk. I mean, if I'm worth millions just for saying "Dada," think what I would be worth for reciting *Anne of Green Gables* in English and French. But let's lead them on gradually—just small words at first.

PROFESSOR LINDERS: You mean baby talk?

BABY: Exactly. We could hire Midge as coach. Now I guess I'd better get back into the cage. They should be here any minute. (*BABY reaches for some bananas*.) I'll take a few of these—just for atmosphere. Do I look all right?

PROFESSOR LINDERS: You look fine.

BABY: It's funny, but I feel a little nervous. I mean, I'm about to become a big star, right? (*She enters the cage*.)

PROFESSOR LINDERS (*locking the cage*): Yes, I guess we both are. (*The door bursts open and ROBERTS rushes in*.)

ROBERTS: The reporters and photographers and television people will be here any minute. What a story! They're really excited. (*DOCTOR KING enters*.)

DOCTOR KING: The Prime Minister is flying in from Ottawa to have his picture taken with Baby. The provincial Premier wants to have lunch with her on Thursday. And the president of the university is going to give her a special degree!

PROFESSOR LINDERS: A degree in what?

DOCTOR KING: Language arts, of course! (*Looks at BABY*.) Linders, can't you comb her hair or something? How about a ribbon or a barrette?

PROFESSOR LINDERS: No, I think she's fine just as she is.

DOCTOR KING: Maybe next month we can have her teeth straightened. (*BABY squawks and rattles the bars of her cage*.) All right, settle down in there. Oh, I forgot to ask—is she still talking, Linders? Has she said anything else?

PROFESSOR LINDERS (*pauses . . . looks at BABY for a long time. BABY looks back, waiting*): No, she's still only saying "Dada."

DOCTOR KING: What do you mean *only*? It's the greatest breakthrough in the history of science. (*MIDGE knocks on the door and enters*.)

MIDGE: The reporters are all here, Doctor King. There's a real crowd of them. Shall I let them in?

DOCTOR KING: Yes, let them in. (*MIDGE opens the doors. About a dozen reporters, photographers, and TV journalists and camera operators come in.*

There's great confusion while they set up their equipment and take their positions. After a moment or so, DOCTOR KING holds up his hand for silence.) Ladies and gentlemen, welcome to the University of Scientific Studies. I think that what we have here can safely be called the Story of the Century. May I present, Baby—the world's first talking chimpanzee. (*Silence falls over the room as all the reporters train cameras and microphones on BABY.*)

BABY (*looks dramatically over the crowd, and then reaches through the bars to take DOCTOR KING'S hand*): Dada! (*The reporters burst into applause, and cameras flash. DOCTOR KING again holds up his hand for silence.*)

DOCTOR KING: And I'd particularly like you to meet the dedicated scientist whose years of hard work have paid off so handsomely. She is an inspiration to us all. Ladies and gentlemen, please meet Professor Hannah Linders! (*More applause and pictures taken as PROFESSOR LINDERS walks over to the cage. She looks at BABY. BABY looks back, and then reaches through the bars to take PROFESSOR LINDERS' hand.*)

BABY (*whispers*): Partners?

PROFESSOR LINDERS (*smiling, whispers back*): Partners. (*More applause and camera flashes as the curtain falls.*)

THE END

JOURNEY THROUGH THE STARS

by Clive Endersby

Episode Three:
The Sky Watchers

It has been three days by our atomic clock since we left the Silent Planet. We do not know where we are, or even if we're headed in the right direction. The others are being very brave, but sometimes I think we will never see the earth again. What if we're trapped in this spaceship forever?

Ruth stopped writing and rubbed her aching fingers. It had taken her a long time to write about all the adventures that she and her sister and their friends had had. But she felt it was important to keep a record of their extraordinary journey.

Ruth had written down everything she could remember about the strange two-headed creature that had captured her and her sister, Karen, in the Science Museum. She described how the creature had sent them—along with Jeff, Rita, and Tony—to a distant planet in another galaxy. Then she explained that the people living on that planet had provided the five of them with a spaceship programmed to seek out all planets with an earth-like atmosphere.

"Oh, I'll never get it right!" came Tony's angry voice from the other side of the cabin.

Ruth looked up, closing her diary. Karen was teaching Tony and Rita to speak in sign language. As usual, Tony's mistakes were making him impatient.

"You are both doing great," Karen signed slowly so that Tony would understand.

If only Jeff hadn't given up so easily! Ruth thought to herself.

Just then Jeff's voice rang through the tiny cabin as he burst in from the sleeping quarters. "Hey, everybody, look what I made!" he shouted proudly, waving a fancy cardboard crown.

"Very interesting," giggled Rita. "Are you planning to crown yourself king?"

Jeff shook his head. "I was bored, so I thought we'd make up a play about Queen Victoria."

"You wouldn't be so bored," Tony piped up, "if you tried to learn some sign language."

"Aw, it's too hard," Jeff replied. He grabbed Ruth's pen and drew some sparkly jewels on his home-made crown.

Rita's fingers started moving and the others began to laugh.
"What's so funny?" Jeff demanded.
"I told Karen that you're smart but lazy," Rita replied.
Jeff strode across the cabin and good-naturedly plonked the crown on Rita's head.
"For that smart remark, Rita, you get to play Queen Victoria!"
Suddenly Karen's hand shot up. She'd felt a change in the vibrations of the spaceship's engines.
"We're slowing down!" yelled Tony, and they all scrambled towards the small windows.
"Wow! Look at that!" Ruth exclaimed, staring out at the smooth glossy surface of an enormous planet. "It looks like a giant marble."
Soon the five friends felt a small jolt as the spaceship landed. The outside doors opened, and a ladder slid down automatically from the opening. The space travellers clustered in the doorway to get a better view of the planet beneath them. Ruth was right. The planet *did* resemble a shiny silver marble. There were no trees, hills, cities, or people—not even grass. There was nothing at all on the smooth silvery surface.
"Maybe it's ice," suggested Jeff.
"There's only one way to find out," said Rita. Boldly she swung herself out onto the ladder and began to climb down towards the planet's surface.
But climbing down from the spaceship doors was not as easy as Rita had thought it would be. The ladder rungs were far apart, because they had been built for the tall people of the Silent Planet. And to make the descent even more difficult, the last rung ended about two metres above the planet's slick-looking surface. But Rita was a member of her school's gymnastics team, and was strong enough to lower herself by her arms so that at last she was dangling from the bottom rung of the ladder. This narrowed the gap for her final drop.
"Be careful," cautioned Jeff from above.
Rita let go. The others stared . . . and kept on staring.
"What—happened?" stammered Ruth, her voice shaking.

But no one answered. They couldn't—they didn't know what to say. Rita had simply disappeared.

Rita was bewildered, too. She was so bewildered that she forgot to be frightened. For Rita had landed on the side of a steep hill in the middle of a beautiful park. The spaceship was nowhere in sight. Amazingly, she was standing on ordinary grass, not on the silvery surface she had seen from the ship.

"Jeff! Ruth!" Rita shouted. "Can you hear me?"

There was no answer. Rita glanced around, wondering what to do. Maybe she should sit down and think for a minute. As she did so, she noticed that her belt buckle was missing. The belt was still there, but the buckle seemed to have been torn off.

"That's really weird," Rita said out loud, checking the rest of her clothes and all her pockets. Nothing else was missing. Then she remembered the universal translator. Her hand darted towards her neck. But the funny little metal box and chain were gone!

Fear crept into Rita's stomach. The translator had been a gift from the people on the Silent Planet. It could translate all the strange languages of the universe into English. Without it, Rita knew she probably wouldn't be able to ask anyone on this new planet for help. She began to feel lost and alone. Even though the sun was bright and the day warm, she began to shiver. A tear trickled down her cheek.

The four travellers left behind in the spaceship were still recovering from the shock of seeing their friend disappear. They kept peering down at the planet's surface. Suddenly Ruth spotted Rita's translator lying there on its silvery smoothness. "Maybe we should try to get the translator back," she said. "That way, we might get some clue about what's happened to Rita."

It was too risky, the four friends decided, to climb down and get the translator. They tossed ideas back and forth until Jeff remembered seeing a magnet and some thick plastic cable in the ship's storeroom. Soon the four friends were huddled in the doorway again, watching as Jeff lowered the magnet towards the planet's bright silver surface.

Voices! Rita couldn't believe it. She tilted her head slightly and listened as hard as she could. Again she heard the faint sound of voices in the distance. She stood up and looked around. The voices seemed to be coming from the other side of the hill. Rita began to climb its grassy slope. The voices became clearer. Now Rita could hear that they were singing. She stopped. A puzzled frown furrowed her forehead. She pinched herself to make sure she wasn't dreaming. The voices were quite clear now. Rita gasped, for not only were the voices singing in English—but they were singing a nursery rhyme that she knew very well!

> The grand old Duke of York,
> He had ten thousand men.

Rita bolted up the hill, her heart hammering with excitement. Although it seemed impossible, she was convinced she was back on earth. The voices grew louder. As Rita reached the top of the hill, she joined in, singing the rhyme in a joyful shout.

Jeff gave a final tug on the cable, and pulled the magnet up into the ship. It clattered onto the floor.

"The magnet's brought the translator up with it all right," said Tony. "But what's this?" He pulled a flat shiny piece of metal off the magnet.

"It's Rita's belt buckle," signed Karen.

Tony examined the belt buckle carefully, turning it over and over in his hands. "There are no burn or scorch marks," he observed thoughtfully.

"That's good, isn't it?" Ruth chimed in. "At least we know Rita didn't burn up or anything."

"Do we?" The distress in Tony's voice dashed Ruth's hopes. "Suppose the surface is radioactive or something," Tony continued. "Suppose it instantly vaporizes anything that isn't metal." There was total silence as everyone realized what Tony meant. "That would explain why the bottom of the spaceship didn't disappear," he finished softly. "It's metal too."

"I don't believe that!" Jeff protested. He hurried towards the ladder. "Rita's down there somewhere, and I'm going to find her."

Tony grabbed him. "Don't be stupid! Whatever happened to her will happen to you too. What good would that do?"

"Get out of my way!" Jeff ordered as the two of them toppled to the floor.

"Stop it!" shouted Ruth. "Rita wouldn't have wanted us to fight."

Jeff pushed Tony off him, and they both stared up at Ruth.

"If Rita really is—" Ruth's voice caught, but she forced herself to say what she was thinking. "If she's . . . dead, then going down to the planet wouldn't do any good. All we can do is wait. If she doesn't come back . . ."

Ruth couldn't finish, but they all knew what she meant. They couldn't wait forever. If Rita didn't come back, they would have to go on without her.

And when they were up, they were up.
And when they were down, they were down.
And when they were only halfway up,
They were neither up nor down.

Rita stood at the top of the hill, hardly believing the amazing sights and sounds that greeted her. Hundreds of tiny people were marching towards her. She certainly wasn't back on earth, she realized. Quickly, Rita hid behind a bush, peering out between the leaves. "How will I know if these strange people are friendly?" she asked herself.

None of the little people had noticed Rita's appearance at the top of the hill. They were only about a metre tall, very thin, and dressed identically in brown leather jackets and trousers. Rita realized with a shock that all the faces she could see were covered with smooth, silvery skin. Men, women, and children—all of their faces shimmered in the bright sunshine.

The little people were marching in ten orderly lines. Each line of people was pulling a thick rope attached to a flat platform. The platform rolled along on six pairs of wheels. Riding on top of it was a strange-looking metal object, gleaming in the strong sunlight.

The object was huge—almost 30 m across, and shaped like a gigantic dish. It was covered in shiny metal screens bolted to a frame of metal rods. The dishlike object reminded Rita of the dishes people used to pick up TV signals back on earth, except it was much larger.

The little people positioned their enormous cargo halfway up the steep hillside. Then they secured it by tying the ropes to the sturdy trees that dotted the slope.

As Rita watched from her hiding place, her curiosity grew. Unanswered questions crowded into her mind. Who were these people, and what were they doing with the huge dish? What planet was this? How did these people know the words to an English nursery rhyme? Determined to find out the truth, Rita took a deep breath and stood up.

The effect was immediate. The little people abruptly stopped singing. They stared at Rita. Then, as if on signal, they all rushed towards her, waving their thin, shiny arms and shouting at the tops of their lungs. Rita stood her ground, although she was shaking with fear.

As the first line reached her, the silvery-faced people fell to their knees and pressed their heads to the ground.

"The Queen!" they shouted over and over again. "It's the Queen! Pussycat, pussycat, where have you been? I've been to London to visit the Queen."

Rita relaxed slightly as she realized that the little people didn't seem to have any intention of hurting her. But as more and more of them fell to their knees and joined in the cry, she grew puzzled. "Why do they think I'm a queen?" she wondered. As she scratched her head in bewilderment, her fingers touched the cardboard crown that Jeff had placed on her head. Then she understood. . . .

With every passing minute, Ruth and Jeff and the others back in the spaceship were losing hope. They sat by the door in silence, keeping watch for any sign of Rita. None of them wanted to accept the idea that she had been vaporized when she touched the planet's surface.

Karen began to wonder if Rita might have become invisible instead. She imagined Rita right below them, trying desperately to attract their attention, not knowing that they couldn't see her. It was an awful image. She tugged at Tony's sleeve. Tony turned to her. Karen, moving her fingers very slowly, explained her idea.

Tony shook his head. At first, the idea that Rita might be invisible seemed impossible to him. But as he thought about it, it began to seem more reasonable. He vaguely remembered reading an article about different dimensions occupying the same space. His eyes lit up. He spoke to Karen, his fingers moving as fast as his knowledge of sign language allowed. "Find a pillow," he signalled.

While Karen darted off to the main cabin, Tony untied the magnet from the plastic cable.

"What's up?" asked Jeff.

"Maybe Rita's down there, and we just can't see her," Tony replied as Karen appeared, clutching a large pillow.

While Tony tied the pillow to the cable, he told them what he remembered reading about different dimensions. With renewed hope, the friends were soon lowering the pillow out the ship's door. When the pillow touched the planet's surface, it vanished!

"Watch this!" Tony directed, sounding more confident than he felt. "If the pillow comes back up, it means we can get Rita back, too."

All eyes gazed unblinkingly at the bottom of the cable as Tony began to pull it upwards. They all shouted for joy when the pillow suddenly reappeared, dangling at the end of the cable.

It was the silliest conversation Rita had ever had. After the little people stopped reciting the pussycat rhyme, a bald man with a long pointed chin stepped forward. Very politely, he asked, "Where are you going, my pretty maid?"

"I'm trying to get home to earth," Rita replied. "That's the name of my planet. But I don't know how to get home."

"Home again, home again, jiggety-jig," said a small voice.

Rita turned and saw that the voice belonged to a little boy—even smaller than most of the other little people.

"That's right," Rita told the boy. "That's part of a nursery rhyme that comes from earth. Earth is where I want to go. But I've lost my spaceship."

A woman's head bobbed in excitement, and her kind face creased into a gentle smile. "I saw three ships come sailing by," she began.

"Come sailing by, come sailing by," repeated some of the others. "I saw three ships—"

Rita held up her hand and the chanting stopped. "Not *that* kind of ship," she explained, trying to be patient. "I mean a spaceship. You know, one that flies through the air."

"Lady Bird, Lady Bird, fly away home," said the woman, trying her best to be helpful.

"Yes—yes that's it," stammered Rita. "I want to fly home. I'm lost."

"Little Bo Peep has lost her sheep," piped up a few voices from the edge of the crowd.

Rita was thoroughly confused. Everything the little people said seemed to be part of a nursery rhyme. She couldn't tell if they really understood anything she was saying. "I'm lost," she repeated slowly, "and I don't know what to do. Can you tell me what to do?"

"Humpty Dumpty sat on a wall," one of them replied.

"Doctor Foster went to Gloucester!" shouted another.

"Jack and Jill went up the hill," added a third.

Rita sighed. It was useless, she decided. The little people could not help her. She would have to find some other way of getting back to the ship and earth.

Just then a siren started wailing. The sudden noise caused great excitement among the little people. They began pelting down the hill towards the giant metal dish. The kind woman and the little boy took Rita's hands and led her quickly after the others. "It's time, it's time for a nursery rhyme," the little people chanted over and over.

When Rita reached the dish with the others, she saw that it was a very complicated machine. At its base was a large screen. As the little people gathered excitedly in front of the screen, a picture began to form. A young man appeared on the silvery screen, and his voice boomed out, "And now it's time for our nursery rhyme."

Rita's mouth popped open in surprise because she recognized the man's face. He was the host of a daily television program for young children, back on earth. Rita had seen the program a few times when she was babysitting; she knew that the host recited a nursery rhyme every day. There were always pictures to go with it.

Now she watched, fascinated, as the scene changed to a picture of a royal palace. A queen with a crown on her head and a rolling pin in her hand emerged as the voice began reciting, "The Queen of Hearts, she baked some tarts—"

Rita glanced around. There wasn't a murmur or a movement from the hushed crowd. They were watching so intently that Rita knew they were memorizing the rhyme, word for word.

Rita smiled to herself. Everything was finally beginning to make sense. Somehow, the gigantic dish was picking up a stray television transmission that had been beamed from earth towards one of its circling communications satellites. The earth, the orbiting satellite, and this distant planet must be in the right position to pick up the TV signal for only a few minutes each week. And those few minutes happened to be the nursery rhyme section of the children's program.

Rita's thoughts were interrupted by a sudden harsh buzzing sound. The television voice was lost in a wave of static interference. The picture flickered, and then dissolved to snow.

The young man's voice came back only long enough to state, firmly and clearly:

"...stole those tarts
And took them clean away."

Then the screen went blank, and the machine automatically turned itself off.

Rita noticed with a gasp that every eye had turned from the screen to the crown on her head. A chill swept through her as a woman hissed, "She stole the tarts!"

"She stole the tarts, and took them clean away," came the menacing chant from the others. The whole crowd began moving slowly towards Rita.

Terrified, Rita took a step backward. "It's only a nursery rhyme," she said lamely. "Anyway, it was the *knave* who stole the tarts, not the queen."

But the little people hadn't heard that part of the rhyme. They thought *she* had stolen the tarts. And they seemed very upset about it. What would they do to her? A quick look told her that she was surrounded.

"Ring around a rosy," Rita shouted in desperation. "A pocketful of posies. Husha, husha. We all fall down!"

The little people's chanting suddenly stopped. Rita repeated her rhyme, and this time a few of them joined in. Uncertainly, they began to link hands and dance in a circle. Then, at the end of the rhyme, they all fell to the ground.

It was the moment Rita had been waiting for. She leaped over the group nearest her and started dashing up the hill.

"She stole the tarts!" cried a hundred voices.

Rita glanced over her shoulder at the wave of silver-skinned little bodies surging up the hill behind her. The chase was on. Although she was sure her long legs would keep her ahead of the screaming tide, she knew that she could not run forever. Sooner or later she would have to stop and rest. Already, she was tiring from running uphill.

"This way, Rita, run!"

Rita's head whipped up at the sound of the familiar voice. She could hardly believe her eyes. Standing at the top of the hill, urging her on, was Ruth!

When Rita reached her friend, she sank to the ground, her chest heaving. She tried to catch her breath. "How did you find me?" she managed to gasp.

"I'll tell you later," Ruth said quickly. "Jeff's waiting for us. Come on."

Rita looked down the other side of the hill. Jeff was standing at the spot where she had first landed on the surface of the planet. Beside him was a thick cable that seemed to be hanging in midair. Puzzled, she glanced up at Ruth.

"The cable's tied to the door of the spaceship," explained Ruth impatiently. "But the ship is in another dimension, so we can't see it. Now come on, Rita. They're almost here."

Ruth pulled the exhausted Rita to her feet. Together the two girls started running down towards Jeff just as the first group of angry little people reached the top of the hill.

Rita ran along in a daze. Halfway down the hill, she stumbled, fell, and scraped both knees. Tears welled up in her eyes as blood trickled from a painful gash on her right knee. Behind Rita and Ruth, their pursuers screamed gleefully, quickly narrowing the gap.

Shouting words of encouragement, Ruth hauled Rita to her feet and almost dragged the limping girl along the grassy slope.

Waiting by the cable, Jeff wondered what he should do. He thought the two girls would reach him sooner than the mob, but he wasn't sure all three of them would have time to get up the cable before the mob caught up with them. It seemed sensible for him to save time by climbing the cable now. But he didn't want to leave his friends in trouble. He hesitated for a few seconds, and then he heard Ruth's voice urging him, "Go, Jeff, go!"

Ruth's shout propelled Jeff into action. Wrapping his legs around the slippery cable, he clambered upwards, hand over hand.

The two girls reached the cable just as Jeff disappeard.

"You first," panted Ruth, pointing upwards.

But Rita shook her head. "I can't! I've got to catch my breath."

Ruth realized Rita was right. The injured girl was completely tired out. Ruth grabbed the cable and began to climb. "When you can't see me anymore," she shouted down to Rita, "tie the cable around yourself and hold on. We'll pull you up! You won't have to climb at all."

Rita did as she was told. When Ruth had vanished, she tied the rope under her arms. Now there was nothing to do but wait. "She stole the tarts!" howled the little people threateningly. Only a few metres now separated them from the exhausted girl. Rita closed her eyes so that she couldn't see the fierce anger on their thin, shiny faces.

Suddenly there was a sharp tug on the cable. Rita felt herself being pulled slowly upwards. One of the little people made a frantic lunge for her legs. But Rita quickly swung them out of the way. Then her foot was caught by the woman who had spoken so kindly to her before. Anger now twisted the woman's face. For a terrible moment Rita hovered in midair, a human link in a tug-of-war between her unseen friends above and the howling mob below. The cable cut into her underarms as she felt herself being pulled downwards.

Then, all at once, she was free of the screaming little people. Higher and higher she rose, until at last she could see the spaceship looming above her.

Jeff, Tony, and Karen were crowded in the doorway, pulling on the cable with all their might. Ruth was waiting anxiously on the ladder. When Rita came within reach, Ruth steadied her on a ladder rung and untied the cable.

"It's only a few more rungs now, Rita," Ruth said gently. "Can you make it?"

Rita nodded, tears of relief flooding her eyes. Together she and Ruth climbed up the remaining rungs to their waiting friends.

"Close the door," Tony told Jeff, pulling Rita and Ruth inside the spaceship. "Let's get out of here fast!"

Rita had little strength left, but she raised her arm and pointed in the direction she remembered the satellite dish had been facing. "That way," she said weakly. "I think the earth is that way."

Tony ran off to the control room. A few minutes later there was a mighty thrust, and then the familiar throb of the ship's engines.

Karen had found some antiseptic in the ship's first-aid kit and was carefully dabbing at Rita's scraped knees. She was bandaging the gash on Rita's right knee when she caught her sister's eye and pointed at Rita's foot.

"You lost your shoe," exclaimed Ruth.

Rita looked down and wiggled her toes. The strap must have

broken when the woman was trying to pull her down. She shuddered as she realized how close she had come to being caught by the angry mob.

"And you lost my cardboard crown, too," complained Jeff jokingly.

Rita smiled. "I always thought it would be fun to be a queen," she said, and then she began to laugh. "But after today, I don't think I'd ever want to be one—not even in a play."□

Feeling a bit more hopeful of reaching their destination, the five young friends settled down to continuing their journey through space. Maybe one day they would return to earth—in time to warn others about the creature that had sent them off to this strange galaxy so far from home.

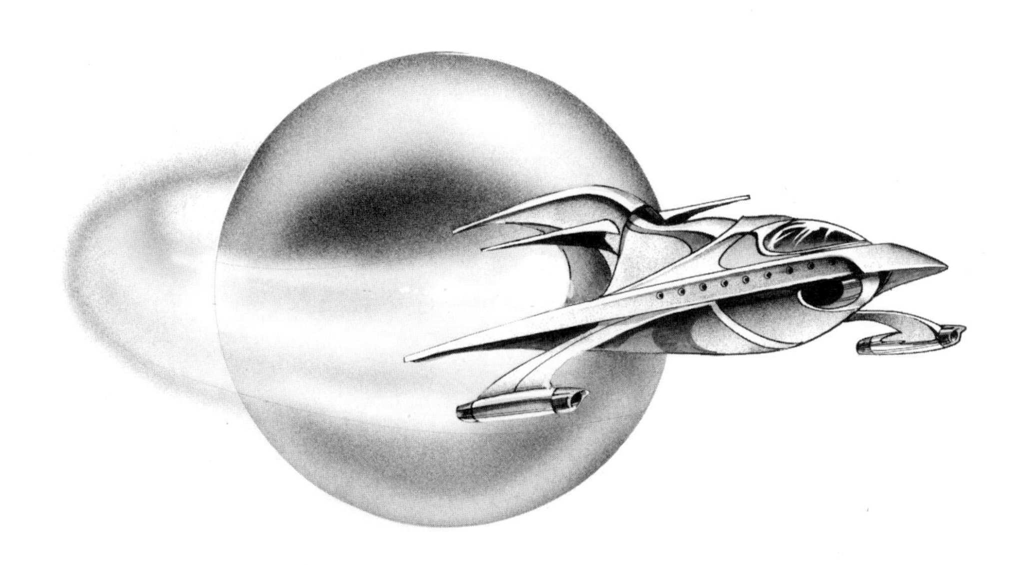

234567890/AP/0987654